THE NATURALIST IN CENTRAL SOUTHERN ENGLAND

HAMPSHIRE, BERKSHIRE, WILTSHIRE, DORSET and SOMERSET

In the same series

THE NATURALIST IN DEVON
AND CORNWALL
by Roger Burrows

THE NATURALIST IN THE ISLE OF MAN
by Larch S. Garrad

THE NATURALIST IN WALES
by R. M. Lockley

THE REGIONAL NATURALIST

THE NATURALIST IN

Central Southern England

HAMPSHIRE, BERKSHIRE, WILTSHIRE, DORSET and SOMERSET

DERRICK KNOWLTON

DAVID & CHARLES : NEWTON ABBOT

TO MY WIFE

0 7153 5876 6

Set in 12 on 13pt Bembo
and printed in Great Britain
by Latimer Trend & Company Ltd Plymouth
for David & Charles (Holdings) Limited
South Devon House Newton Abbot Devon

Contents

List of Illustrations

Plates

IN TEXT

Introduction

One of the difficulties in writing a book of this kind is to decide what must be left out, so great is the embarrassment of riches. For example, the county of Wiltshire alone has over 1,000 kinds of flowering plants and nearly 75 per cent of the total number of species of British insects; Somerset has 1,440 of the moths and butterflies on the British list; the Isle of Wight has half the total number of species comprising the beetle fauna of the country, and the abundance of invertebrate life in the New Forest is known far beyond the confines of the British Isles.

Inevitably it becomes a matter of personal choice and no two people would make the same selection. In general, I have sought to describe the various communities by giving as balanced a selection as possible of the various plants and animals. Some of the uncommon species have been included as well since most naturalists thrill to the unusual and there is no reason why they should not, provided that they do not become mere tally-hunters, despising the commonplace.

It is clear that no one person could possibly have an encyclopaedic knowledge of the wild life of any district, however small, and I have been greatly assisted by the recorded observations of hundreds of naturalists to whom I gladly acknowledge my indebtedness. Detailed acknowledgement to those who have directly helped me in various ways is made at the end of the book.

Much remains to be discovered about the natural history of the region. Naturalists, whether resident or visiting, are never likely to exhaust the possibilities of nature study. Despite the work already done, discoveries of species new to the region are still being made and even, on occasion, of species new to the British list.

The floristic and faunal importance of the region derives partly from its geographical situation. Its proximity to the mainland of Europe coupled with the mildness of the climate has enabled continental species to establish a foothold, whilst the Lusitanian species, that is the south-west European element, extend eastwards into the region.

Although this is a heavily populated region there are many acres where the naturalist can wander without let or hindrance, indeed without meeting many people. Such are the 90 square miles of the New Forest, parts of the downland, the Quantocks, the Mendips and many acres of heathland. The whole area is patterned with a multitude of footpaths, including the prehistoric Ridgeway which stretches for many miles through Wiltshire and Berkshire, canal towpaths, clifftop walks, peat tracks in the Somerset fens and an increasing number of nature trails. In addition, the bona-fide naturalist is not likely to encounter difficulty in gaining access to private land provided he first exercises the elementary courtesy of seeking permission and thereafter shows the consideration that he would expect to receive himself.

Despite the occasional usefulness of a car as a mobile hide, a boat from which to count sea bird colonies, or even an aeroplane for making a census of swans, most observations must be made on foot. The study of nature becomes more and more sophisticated; the range of equipment available increases yearly and naturalists find themselves expected to be, amongst other things, statisticians. But no matter what the degree of sophistication, the observing of wild life continues to be the sublimation of the hunting instinct. My hope is that a reading of this book will send the reader out into the field, and I wish him good hunting.

CHAPTER ONE

An outline of the region

Scenery–Climate–Geology–Distinguished naturalists of the past

BETWEEN THE SOUTH-WEST peninsula and south-east England lies an amorphous slab of country loosely known as central southern England. It lacks the cohesive unity of the Celtic West and although it possesses more affinity with the lands of the South Saxons and of the Jutes in the Garden of England it nevertheless differs from them in ways not easy to define.

For example, when the meteorologist forecasts rain for the South West and sunshine for the South East, those of us who live halfway between must make our own choice, depending on whether we are of pessimistic or optimistic temperament.

How then are we to think of this region, and is there any homogeneity in shires so diverse as Hampshire, Berkshire, Wiltshire, Dorset and Somerset? Back in about the year AD 500, the West Saxon chief Cerdic and his son Cynric beached their boats on the south-east shore of the New Forest, moved north-westwards and by 527 had established themselves in Hampshire and at least part of Wiltshire. Meanwhile further north other West Saxons were forcing their way westwards along the Thames valley, thereby unknowingly beating the northern bounds of our region. Armed detachments fanned out south-westwards and it was only a matter of time before the kingdom of Wessex was founded, with Winchester as its capital.

The precise extent of Wessex is shrouded in obscurity. Certainly it was not exactly co-terminous with the area covered by this book but, by and large, the ancient kingdom and the modern region cover much the same ground. Here then is the historical backbone holding the component parts together. Amidst the heterogeneous races which make up the population of central southern England, West Saxon is the dominant racial type. There is a structural backbone to the region as well, a unity of the landscape originating in the calcareous mud and marine life of seas from the Carboniferous period of 250 million years ago to the Upper Cretaceous of 70 million years ago. In other words, chalk and other forms of limestone provide much of the scenery, particularly the chalk.

Conspicuous features of southern England are the rounded contours of the downs, rolling from one white-topped crest to the next like the waves of an earthen sea, the denuded summits mimicking the 'white horses' of the spume. The white horses carved on the chalk, numbers of them, lie below on the scarp face. The often dry chalk valleys between the ridges hold attractive but unpretentious villages. Where grassland remains on the slopes above, it is dotted white with sheep; and on the skyline, as like as not, are isolated clumps of beeches. This is the soft South Country of Jefferies, Hudson and White. It is a land where the south-west wind blows warmly and nature smiles; a land in which it is good to live.

Further west the chalk's hold on the land structure vanishes and a very diversified landscape appears with the patchwork quilt of the Somerset plain, the heathery summits of the Quantocks and the low-lying fens around Glastonbury; but even here limestone is far from absent, forming the Mendips, the fenland knolls and much of Dorset.

The boundaries of the region are easily described. In the south, the boundary is the coastline between Lyme Regis in Dorset and Hayling Island in Hampshire, then from the junction of Somerset and Dorset just north of Lyme Regis it follows the Somerset boundary north-westwards over the Blackdown Hills and (Exmoor being included in another volume of this series), strikes north along the western slopes of the Quantocks to the sea at Quantockshead and along the Bristol Channel coast north-eastwards to Portishead. From there it first follows the Avon and then for most of the way the line of the Thames to Windsor where the eastern boundary runs south to Hayling Island.

The six administrative counties are:

County	*Area (to nearest sq mile)*
Somerset	1,613
Hampshire	1,503
Wiltshire	1,344
Dorset	978
Berkshire	725
Isle of Wight	147

The highest hill is Will's Neck in the Quantocks, 1,261ft, and much of the Mendips is at the 1,000ft level. But in only a few places elsewhere does the land exceed 900ft, notably on the Hampshire–Berkshire border and on the northern flank of the Vale of Pewsey in Wiltshire, though there are many hills above 800ft.

Climate

The climate is equable, with generally mild winters and fairly warm if not always fine summers. The prevailing winds blow from the south-west bringing rainfall which varies from 45in on the hills of Somerset and in western Dorset to under 30in along the south Hampshire coast. Conditions are naturally bleaker and colder on the exposed downs than in the sheltered valleys. In 1888 the Wiltshire botanist the Reverend T. A. Preston described the winds that cut across the Marlborough Downs in a delightfully illuminating phrase as 'east winds blowing from the west'. Of the six counties Berkshire has the most bracing climate and in contrast the lower valley of the Bristol Avon probably has the highest humidity.

Climate, of course, has a tremendous effect on wild life. Microclimates of a few square yards may influence the siting of plants; cold winters may protect insect pupae from predatory birds whilst killing great numbers of larger animals; the fruiting

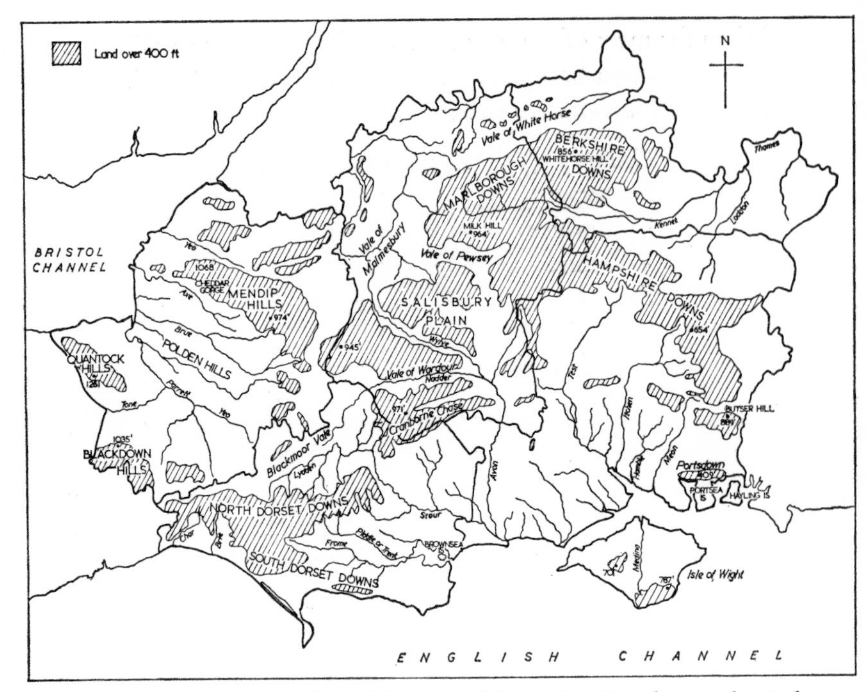

Map showing principal physical features of the region. Based upon the Ordnance Survey Map with the sanction of the Controller of HM Stationery Office, Crown copyright reserved

bodies of fungi are much more in evidence during a wet autumn. The effect of weather is perhaps most noticeable on bird life: a sudden severely cold spell inevitably brings a great influx of birds, notably wildfowl from frozen waters further north, and large flocks of lapwings, thrushes and skylarks are often seen. Long-term climatic changes are less easy to discern and their influence even harder to gauge but there can be little doubt that they affect species living on the edge of their range. The conspicuous decline of wryneck and red-backed shrike within the region in recent years may come into this category.

As is well known, lichens are good natural pollution indicators. An examination of the distribution of lichens in Hampshire has shown that although there is some degree of pollution in the

Page 17 (*above*) Priddy Pools on the Mendips—gorse and ling on exposed core of Old Red Sandstone contrast with pasture on Carboniferous Limestone in the distance, the pool in centre choked with horsetail, sedge and cotton grass; (*below*) the fertile Lias farmland of the Somerset plain from Ham Hill

Page 18 (*above*) Goblin Combe—wood sage in foreground, young sessile oak left centre with whitebeam behind, spindle with old man's beard far right; (*below*) fossilised wood from the Bagshot Sand in Hampshire

coastal towns, as evidenced by lichen scarcity, the New Forest remains unaffected as proved by the abundance of species.

Geology

A man travelling north-west from Southampton to Portishead passes over a succession of rock formations in descending order, that is of increasing age if drift deposits are ignored At the start. of his journey he is on Bracklesham beds but within a few miles the Bagshot Sands are reached and then successive beds of Eocene strata are traversed until he comes to the Upper Chalk outcrops in the vicinity of Salisbury. Due to the dip of the rocks Middle and Lower Chalk next appear, followed by Upper Greensand and Gault in the neighbourhood of Warminster. A narrow band of Cornbrash is succeeded by a much wider belt of Great Oolite Limestone between Frome and Radstock. Here the coal measures begin, but are much overlaid by Lower Lias rocks and Triassic marls. At Dundry Hill an outlier of Upper Lias and Inferior Oolite is crossed, and after a further area of Lias and Triassic strata a belt of Carboniferous Limestone is traversed south-west of Bristol followed by a narrow band of Old Red Sandstone, the oldest bed exposed on this traverse. New Red Sandstone marls reappear for the rest of the route to Portishead. The traveller has journeyed about 100 miles in space and some 250 million years in time.

The geological term 'Hampshire Basin' is misleading because the basin covers much of Dorset and Wiltshire as well. Its formation began in the Alpine earth movements of Tertiary times when, under great pressure, the central part of that area, the Weald, rose in a dome-shaped mass. The resultant hollows or synclines on each side are known as the Hampshire and London Basins. A small part of the London Basin lies within the southern central region in north-east Hampshire and south-east Berkshire, giving rise to sandy heathland. The Hampshire Basin, by contrast, is a prominent feature, the wide rim formed by the north Dorset downs, Salisbury Plain and the north Hampshire downs dipping under the lowlands and the Solent to emerge as the southern rim in the Isle of Wight chalk. The 'pudding' in the Basin consists of a number of wedge-shaped alternate fluviatile and marine deposits of which in general only the latter are fossiliferous, although fossilised drift wood and leaf impressions are found in the Bagshot Sands. These Tertiary deposits include the famous cliff-face at Barton-on-Sea referred to in Chapter Two (p 51).

The general north-east trend of the strata is well seen in north-western Berkshire, where after the Cretaceous rocks come successive Jurassic beds, Kimmeridge Clay, Corallian Limestone and Oxford Clay. A good place to see almost the whole of the fossiliferous Corallian Limestone in one exposure is at Dry Sandford Quarry, now a nature reserve of the Berkshire, Buckinghamshire and Oxfordshire Naturalists' Trust. Here are corals, sea-urchins, ammonites and many a lamellibranch and gastropod. Another interesting locality is at Faringdon, where gravels in the Lower Greensand contain many fossil sponges and marine shells. These gravels carry a distinctive lichen community, as do the sarsen stones on the Marlborough Downs in Wiltshire.

Whilst about 25 per cent of Berkshire consists of chalk there is more than 50 per cent in Wiltshire forming the northern rim of the Hampshire Basin, although the chalk is covered with clay-with-flints in many areas. In 1963 a fossil coelacanth *Macropoma mantelli* was discovered near Westbury. Ten years earlier a living coelacanth 5ft long and weighing 100lb was caught off the Comoro Islands between the African mainland and Madagascar—only the second specimen caught in recent years of this fish, hitherto believed to have been extinct for 50 million years.

North of Salisbury Plain lies the Vale of Pewsey. Although now a valley between chalk hills it is in fact a denuded part of an anticline which extends eastwards to the Hog's Back in Surrey. It is probable that an ancient river once flowed through the vale. Anticlines are lines of weakness susceptible to denudation: the

Vale of Wardour and the low ground at Warminster are further examples of denuded anticlines in Wiltshire. In the Vale of Wardour the outcropping Purbeck and Portland beds, containing the usual Portland fossil fauna of ammonites and large lamellibranchs, are quarried. The Bath Freestone which is quarried in the neighbourhood of Corsham is Jurassic Limestone from the Great Oolite beds.

The area of principal geological interest in Dorset is the coast, briefly referred to in Chapter Two (p 55). There has been extensive test drilling for oil in Dorset and Hampshire, mainly since World War II, although a bore was sunk on the Portsdown anticline just north of Portsmouth in the 1930s. The only commercial success so far is at Kimmeridge in Dorset, where the first borehole was sunk in March 1959 and at a depth of 1,816ft oil was located in the Cornbrash; production began in 1961.

At Swanage and its hinterland in the Isle of Purbeck, east Dorset, there is an area of sands, shales and marls of the Wealden beds. Below the Wealden are the beds of Purbeck Limestone including the red and green Purbeck marbles which are not true marbles but shelly limestones. At Ballard Point is a conspicuous example of a thrust fault in the chalk. The centre of Dorset consists of a broad diagonal belt of chalk from Askerswell on the Dorchester–Bridport road through Blandford to Cranborne Chase. An interesting phenomenon in the chalk country around Briantspuddle near Dorchester is the formation of a number of swallow holes caused by sub-surface denudation of the chalk. The largest, known as Cull-peppers Dish, is 100yd wide and 40ft deep. Further west are Jurassic Limestones with a considerable area of Lias rocks around Lyme Regis.

South Somerset is not perhaps so well known as the northern part of the county, but it is equally beautiful. The deeply sunken lanes of the Lias sands are a feature of the countryside around Yeovil, as are the isolated ridges of the limestone hills rising above the chequered field-pattern of the Somerset plain. Another pseudo-marble, a limestone crowded with small ammonites and known as Marston marble, used to be quarried at

Marston Magna near Ilchester. Upper Lias beds with fossil fish occur at Ilminster.

In north Somerset there are coalmines around Radstock, the Carboniferous strata lying in a syncline mainly overlain at the surface by marls of New Red Sandstone. Coalmining in this district is of great antiquity and may have been practised by the Romans. In some places there are volcanic olivine-basalt lavas in the Carboniferous series. In the Jurassic rocks south of Bath are beds of fullers earth which is extracted for a variety of commercial uses. The hot springs (120° F, 49° C) at Bath are well known.

During the Armorican earth movements which took place in late Carboniferous times the Mendips were formed. These are of Carboniferous Limestone with underlying strata of Old Red Sandstone exposed in some places. In the eastern Mendips not only the Carboniferous Limestone but also the Old Red Sandstone has been removed, exposing a small area of Silurian rocks, the oldest formation in the region. Some of this consists of volcanic rocks and some of mudstones rich in fossils. In hollow nodules in Dolomitic Conglomerate of the New Red Sandstone and in Carboniferous veins are found rock crystals known as Bristol Diamonds. Rock crystal is a pure form of quartz and occurs in several colours; it is still collected and sold in jewellers' shops.

Distinguished naturalists of the past

From the eighteenth century onward the region has had its dedicated naturalists who laid sound foundations for those who came after. Mention can only be made of a handful of the best known. The first to be mentioned must surely be the Hampshire naturalist Gilbert White, born in 1720 at Selborne in eastern Hampshire. For a considerable time he was curate of the neighbouring parish of Faringdon and it was not until he was sixty-four that he was appointed curate of his beloved Selborne. A scholarly man with a love of the simple rural life, he was content

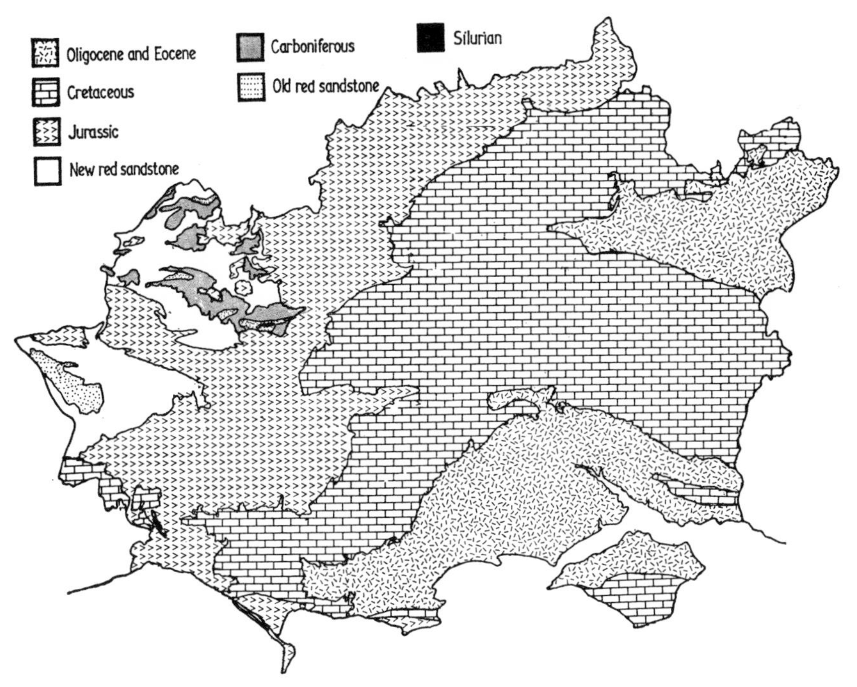

Geological map showing the periods represented in the region. Crown copyright. Based on Geological Survey map. Reproduced by permission of Director, IGS

to let opportunities of preferment pass by and find fulfilment in meticulous observations of nature, observations which he recorded in unassuming style but with great accuracy in letters written to a friend. These letters later became his celebrated book *The Natural History of Selborne*, published when he was sixty-eight.

W. H. Hudson spent much time in Hampshire and Wiltshire in his later years. The New Forest drew him like a magnet but he spent a considerable amount of time wandering in the Itchen valley and over the eastern heathland. He was one of the early conservationists; bird protection was a subject dear to his heart and one for which he actively campaigned. It is fitting, therefore, that his memory is preserved not only by his books but by a bird sanctuary in Hyde Park named after him.

Richard Jefferies, a contemporary of Hudson, lived at Coate, near Swindon, his house now being a museum. His was a short life, a mere thirty-nine years, spent in poverty and declining health, but he had a passionate love of nature and enjoyed to the full the country pursuits about which he wrote with such feeling and discernment.

A writer of a different kind was E. W. Swanton, an enthusiastic naturalist with the capacity to inspire enthusiasm in others. He was born in 1870 at Dibden in south Hampshire and became curator of Haslemere Educational Museum when he was twenty-seven. He wrote factual books on various aspects of natural history—his *British Plant Galls*, for instance, published in 1912—and contributed to the study of Wiltshire molluscs.

These were writers all. Mary Anning was not. She was born in 1799 in Lyme Regis, the daughter of a cabinetmaker, and as a child she accompanied her father when he pursued his hobby of fossil collecting along the sea cliffs. This was a pastime he was able to turn to profitable account by selling his finds. He died when Mary was only ten years old, and in desperate poverty this pathetic child was driven to the only occupation of which she had experience; she soon made her first sale, an ammonite for half a crown. Necessity quickly made her precocious and shrewd but the physical prowess and skill she displayed in locating and extracting fossils was remarkable.

Urged on by her brother who had made the discovery, she excavated from the shore the first complete skeleton of the marine reptile *Ichthyosaurus*. Considerable scientific interest was now aroused and subsequently in addition to her routine collecting she dug out a *Pterodactyl* and a *Plesiosaurus*.

Mary Anning was an exemplar of Emerson's aphorism, 'If a man can write a better book, preach a better sermon or make a better mouse-trap, though he build his house in the woods, the world will make a beaten track to his door.' Geologists, palaeontologists, even a king, came to her door and the prime minister gave her a grant from the civil list in recognition of her work. But she became crippled with rheumatism and died of cancer when only forty-eight; so ended the extraordinary career of the 'fossil woman' of Lyme.

A few years before Mary Anning was born, a young man in Somerset was discovering the basic principles of stratigraphy. William Smith, justifiably known as the father of English geology, was born in Oxfordshire, outside this central southern region, but it was whilst working as a surveyor on the construction of the Somerset Coal Canal that he arrived at the concept of rock succession with all that this implied. His geological map of the district around Bath is the oldest geological map known. He was a resourceful man of great intellect and, quite apart from his discoveries, was in great demand as a skilled engineer. Like Mary Anning he too amassed a great collection of fossils, but in the service of stratigraphy rather than palaeontology.

Another geologist who studied the rocks of Somerset was Charles Moore who was born at Ilminster in 1815 but whose main work was done in the neighbourhood of Bath. He deserves mention for his discovery both of the earliest known British mammal *Microleptus moorei* and of the Rhaetic bed from which it came. This involved the purchase of some three tons of clay and the methodical sifting of this material for several hours a day over a number of years; amongst many other fossil fragments Moore also found over 70,000 fish scales belonging to one genus alone—Herculean labours indeed!

Among geologists of more recent times was Arthur Vaughan, a master at a training school for potential army officers at Bristol who in his spare time carried out with masterly skill an analysis of the zonal divisions of the Carboniferous Limestone in the Avon gorge. Not the least important aspect of this achievement was that it initiated further research and enabled advances of knowledge to be made.

The region had many capable botanists in the last century and a number of floras were produced. Perhaps Frederick Townsend, Fellow of the Linnaean Society and author of *The Flora of*

Hampshire, 1883, was one of the most outstanding. He lived in Hampshire for nine years, in the village of Shedfield, and before that at Great Bedwyn in Wiltshire where he made a collection of molluscs. But there were botanists in the region before the last century. Little need be said about the rather erratic enthusiasms of John Aubrey, the Wiltshire naturalist of the early seventeenth century, except to note that he was the first person to compile a list of Wiltshire plants. Belonging to this period also was the Hampshire botanist John Goodyear. He was born at Alton in 1592, subsequently moving to Petersfield. The creeping lady's tresses *Goodyera repens* was named after him. In the following century lived William Curtis (1746–99) the botanist and entomologist of Alton in whose honour the town's small museum is named.

Moving to an entirely different field we cannot overlook the famous arachnologist the Reverend O. Pickard-Cambridge who lived at Bloxworth in Dorset where in the latter half of the nineteenth century he followed his father as rector. He not only published a book, *The Spiders of Dorset*, but many important scientific papers and described no fewer than 116 species which were new to science. His many other interests included the whole field of natural history. Dr W. S. Bristowe has described him as the greatest British arachnologist of all time. He died in 1917.

Another diligent Dorset naturalist of more modern times was the entomologist Dr C. D. Day (1885–1968). In the first half of this century he amassed a magnificent collection of insects of a number of orders. He bequeathed a fine twenty-drawer collection of Dorset insects to Dorchester Museum, and the collection of 3,000 flies of the family Tachinidae in which he specialised (a further indication of his industry), is now distributed amongst twenty-six universities and museums.

In the heyday of the last century the New Forest was visited by many lepidopterists of national status who published many a paper in entomological journals on the forest insect fauna. Finally, it can be the region's proud claim that within its boundaries, at Sandown on the Isle of Wight, Charles Darwin began the writing of his momentous *Origin of Species* which was to make such a revolutionary change in man's whole approach to nature.

CHAPTER TWO

The coastline

South coast beaches, dunes, salt marshes, estuaries and cliffs–The Somerset coast

THE COAST OF the region is very varied, though it might as well be admitted from the start that some sections from a scenic point of view are rather dull. Rocky pools, bright with anemones, are relatively few and in the many miles of fine cliffs there is a scarcity of the popular flower-studded type with accessible sandy beach.

There are, however, many scenes of striking beauty. The Isle of Wight, for example, has magnificent coastal scenery. On a day of winter sunshine I have stood on the height above Littlesea in Dorset and longed to be able to capture on canvas the wild beauty of the marshy lagoons dotted with Bewick swans and fringed with straw-coloured reeds set in the silver of Shell Bay, a remote landscape almost inconceivable on the populous south coast. On stormy days people travel for miles to see the inspiring spectacle of waves breaking over the rugged rocks of Portland Bill. But to the naturalist, scenic values are a welcome bonus, not an essential ingredient. To him, the interest of the southern littoral stems from the great variety of habitat and a number of unusual natural features.

Portsdown Hill is the conspicuous ridge of chalk immediately behind Portsmouth Harbour. Alpine earth movements brought up this chalk mass in an anticlinal fold and subsequent erosion denuded the dome of the overlying Tertiary strata which still exists in the lowland to the north. Once this hill was a sea cliff and the remains of an ancient beach lie at about the 100ft level, below Nelson's monument. Southwards lies a coastal plain of alluvium and brickearth salvaged from the sea. Here are three large sea inlets, the harbours of Portsmouth, Langstone and Chichester. Only the western half of the latter is within the region under consideration, the eastern boundary of which is formed by the Emsworth Channel. West of the industrialised area of Portsmouth and its environs the coastline trends north-westwards past the Meon and Hamble estuaries to the drowned valley of Southampton Water with its famous double tides caused by the position of the Isle of Wight, the secondary tide arriving two hours later round Spithead.

Alternating shingle beaches and mudflats intersected by the estuaries of the Beaulieu and Lymington rivers lead south-westwards to the long shingle spit of Hurst which projects some two miles into the Solent and considerably narrows the shipping channel. Sandy cliffs of the Barton Beds now appear and stretch for over six miles until Christchurch Harbour is reached. This is a natural harbour resulting from the confluence of the Avon and the Stour. The resort complex of Bournemouth with its suburbs occupies the next nine miles until we reach another natural inlet of the sea, Poole Harbour, with its cluster of islands of which Brownsea is the foremost.

The sand dunes which began east of the harbour at Sandbanks have on the west side at Shell Bay developed over the last 200 years into a remarkably fine series of dunes rich in plant and animal life. Low Tertiary cliffs south of Studland village soon give place to the seaward outcrop of the chalk range of the Purbeck Hills. Generally as we travel westwards we are descending the geological strata although the configuration of the coastline at times complicates the pattern. Underneath the chalk lies the same formation as occupies much of Sussex and Kent and the sheltered hinterland of Swanage Bay consists of these Wealden Beds.

Now a fine series of cliffs of greatly varying composition ranging from sand, clay, marl, shale to chalk and limestone stretch for some twenty miles or so between Swanage and Weymouth. Here the Jurassic rocks of Portland Bill project some seven miles into the English Channel and at the western end of the base of the promontory there begins the Chesil beach, a shingle deposit stretching for eighteen miles westwards as far as Bridport and one of the most notable features of the English coastline. Its distinguishing peculiarity is the remarkable gradation of pebbles; these are large at the eastern end but gradually lessen in size to the pea gravel at Burton Bradstock. Differing theories have been postulated from time to time to account for this. The principal suggestion appears to be that it is due to the sorting action of the waves, but if this is so it is difficult to understand why it does not happen on other shingle beaches. Beyond Burton Bradstock a varied succession of cliffs culminates in the Blue Lias of Lyme Regis where the county boundary between Dorset and Devon is reached, which is also the western boundary of our region.

South coast beaches

Many of the Hampshire beaches, particularly in the eastern part, are a mixture of sand, shingle and mud. Typical plants include sea kale *Crambe maritima*, yellow horned poppy *Glaucium flavum*, sea beet *Beta vulgaris maritima*, sea campion *Silene maritima*, sea purslane *Halimione portulacoides*, sea rocket *Cakile maritima*, sea sandwort *Honkenya peploides* and in places sea holly *Eryngium maritimum*. The uncommon Nottingham catchfly *Silene nutans* occurs in some quantity at Browndown military ranges, some two miles west of Gosport. Muddy shores support annual sea blite *Suaeda maritima*. On the shingle beach at Gilkicker Point, Gosport, the umbellifer alexanders *Smyrnium olusatrum* is abundant. A group of local bird watchers use this headland at the entrance to Portsmouth Harbour as a migration watchpoint and publish an annual report.

At the western approach to Southampton Water the Hampshire County Council have established a public open space of 113 acres of shingle beach at the Lepe and Calshot foreshore. At the latter place the council have set up a physical activities centre and in conjunction with this a bird hide has been erected on the mudflats in Southampton Water. A considerable variety of plants of shingle, dune and salt marsh can be found at Lepe, including the pellitory of the wall *Parietaria diffusa*. The sea milkwort *Glaux maritima* occurs on muddy sand both here and at Hurst Castle, which is another good botanical locality with a wide range of maritime species although the principal habitat is shingle beach. Here grow several species of orache *Atriplex* spp, saltwort *Salsola kali*, *Geranium purpureum* as well as, more unexpectedly, a plant of calcareous soils, the yellow-wort *Blackstonia perfoliata*, and the uncommon introduced shrub known as the Duke of Argyll's tea-plant *Lycium halimifolium*. The shingle spit here is a good place to watch movements of shore and water birds.

The beaches of Dorset have the same general floristic pattern with minor differences. Sea kale is very scarce but occurs at Bridport, the Chesil beach and Lulworth. The rare shrubby sea blite *Suaeda fruticosa* is plentiful in places in Poole Harbour and the Chesil beach. This last has an interesting flora which includes a maritime form of bittersweet *Solanum dulcamara*, the narrow-flowered thistle *Cardus tenuiflorus*, sea holly, which in Dorset is scarce and is found only along the western half of the coastline, and two rare plants, *Asparagus maritimus* and sea pea *Lathyrus japonica* which in this region is only found here.

On the sea rocket and sea holly along the Dorset coast feed the larvae of the sand dart moth *Agrotis ripae*. The caterpillar feeds through the summer and spends the winter in the larval state burrowed in the sand. Elsewhere in the region it occurs in the Isle of Wight, Hayling Island and on the Somerset coast. Where prickly saltwort grows there may be found both in Hampshire and Dorset the larvae of a local microlepidopteron, *Gymnancyla canella*.

Rocky shores are absent in Hampshire and as a consequence seaweeds are relatively scarce in quantity and species. A fair quantity grows at Hengistbury and at Southsea, including oar weeds *Laminaria* spp, particularly *L. saccharina*; the brown bootlace seaweed *Chorda filum* occurs in places; bladder wrack *Fucus vesiculosus* and saw wrack *F. serratus* are relatively common but the flat wrack *F. spiralis* is scarce although recorded from Warsash. A smaller uncommon brown seaweed of ginger colour, *Halidrys siliquosa*, is found in the more sheltered conditions of Portsmouth Harbour. In the early summer the green seaweed *Enteromorpha* sp is sometimes abundant on tbe mudflats, and the sea lettuce *Ulva lactuca* is also common. The red seaweeds live at the lowest levels and are difficult to identify. Those occurring include the very common *Rhodymenia palmata* and the strong-smelling *Griffithsia corallinoides. Chondrus crispus* has been recorded from the Meon shore. Many more seaweeds are to be found on the rocky shores of Dorset.

Of the molluscs, the bivalves are more typical of the sandy, muddy shores and include several species of cockle *Cardium* spp, variegated scallop *Chlamys varia*, various carpet shells *Venerupis* spp, cut trough shell *Spisula subtruncata* and the blunt gaper *Mya truncata*. The uncommon round double-tooth *Diplodonta rotundata* and the local grooved razor *Solen marginatus* have been recorded from Lepe; *Ensis minor*, the small razor shell, is an uncommon species occurring in Dorset. The prickly cockle *Cardium echinatum* is a local species which has been found at Poole. Most of the tellins *Tellina* spp and venus shells *Venus* spp are scarce or absent from the Hampshire coast but the common oyster *Ostrea edulis* and the common mussel *Mytilus edulis* although not burrowers are fairly frequent, taking advantage of any piers and groynes to which they can attach themselves.

Gastropods such as the limpets *Patella* spp and top shells *Gibbula* spp are inhabitants of rocky shores but they can also be found in smaller numbers along the shingle beaches, as can the periwinkles *Littorina* spp. Towards the end of the last century an American mollusc, the slipper limpet *Crepidula fornicata*, was introduced accidentally with oysters from North America. It is now thoroughly at home on the south coast and extremely abundant on the Hampshire beaches. These limpets are found linked together in chains and possess the extraordinary capacity to change their sex as they grow so that the youngest are always males. Another gastropod is the sting winkle *Ocenebra erinacea*, another predator on oysters. The three severe winters since 1939 have wiped out the south-east coast populations of sting winkle but it is still well-distributed along the south coast beaches in the region.

In Dorset, Shell Bay and Studland beaches have a great variety of molluscs including species which are scarce along the rest of this regional coastline such as the striking pelican's foot *Aporrhais pes-pelecani* and the large necklace *Natica catena*. Lulworth Cove possesses an uncommon species of the coat-of-mail genus *Acanthochitona discrepans* and a top shell *Cantharidus exasperatus* which also occurs at Weymouth. Another top shell *Gibbula lineata* is locally distributed along the Dorset coast.

Various species of bristle worm and sea slug are frequent on the south coast beaches; the shore crab *Carcinus maenas*, hermit crab *Eupagurus* spp and edible crab *Cancer pagurus* are widely distributed and spider crabs occur in places. Sea anemones are generally found only in the rocky sections of the coast but the beadlet *Actinia equina* and the snakelocks *Anemonia sulcata* have been reported from the Meon shore. A sea squirt of warm waters *Styela clava* has been introduced and occurs at Lepe beach and a number of other places. It appears to be increasing and spreading along the coast. Native species of sea squirt abound. A large earwig *Labidura riparia* lives under seaweed on a west Hampshire beach, the only known British station.

The shores of Hampshire and Dorset attract large numbers of birds and many rare species have been observed from time to time. The mudflats of Langstone Harbour, Southampton Water, Pennington Marshes, Stanpit Marsh, Poole Harbour and Ferrybridge, Portland, are good bird localities. All the common species of wader are to be found and the dunlin is the most numerous. The numbers of redshank have not yet fully recovered from the 1963 winter; some spotted redshank occur, particularly in the autumn, at such places as Farlington Marshes and Poole Harbour, but the main locality is Needs Oar where some stay the winter. Small parties of knot occur in winter at various places and probably the largest numbers are seen at Farlington Marshes, but not on the vast scale of east coast flocks. That attractive little wader, the sanderling, occurs in small numbers along the coast particularly during the autumn migration; Poole Harbour and Black Point, Hayling Island are places where sanderling can usually be seen throughout the winter months. Purple sandpiper, that rather drab and colourless bird of the rocks, is a very uncommon species on the southern coastline, but birds have occasionally been seen at Hengistbury Head and small numbers are fairly regular at Portland Bill. Turnstones, which are birds of the shingle, can be seen at Farlington, Meon shore, Warsash and Poole Harbour.

Of the larger waders, grey plover winter in relatively small numbers and can usually be seen at Farlington and Pennington Marshes and Poole Harbour. Black-tailed and bar-tailed godwits are two species which have changed their numerical pattern in this century. Up to the early 1930s the bar-tailed was the commoner of the two. It can be seen today in sizeable flocks at Langstone and Poole Harbours and in much smaller numbers irregularly in a few other places. The black-tailed, however, has increased in numbers and overtaken the bar-tailed, and its distribution is more widespread along the coast. The whimbrel has an unusual wader migration pattern in that more are seen on the spring than on the autumn passage.

Great black-backed gulls are relatively common but lesser black-backed gulls less so. Herring and common gulls are plentiful in winter, often moving inland to feed during the daytime; for example, there is a large diurnal movement of herring, common and black-headed gulls from Southampton Water northwards up the Test and Itchen valleys and north-west to Salisbury Plain. Off-shore the three species of divers winter in small numbers together with red-breasted mergansers, great crested, slavonian, black-necked and red-necked grebes, the last named being the least common. The entrance to Poole Harbour is a good place to look for black-necked grebes in

Page 35 (*above*) Lower Lias cliff at Lyme Regis—Black Ven nature reserve with landslip centre background, rocky shore with rich marine life in foreground; (*below*) bladder wrack with limpet and common periwinkles on the Dorset coast

Page 36 (*above*) Berrow dunes with Steep Holm in right distance; (*below*) *Spartina townsendii* on the Hampshire coast with an immature Sabine's gull, a rare vagrant, in foreground

winter. Of the surface-feeding ducks, wigeons congregate in large rafts off-shore, and of the diving ducks eider is a species which is increasing. Common scoter are seen regularly at Portland Bill and occasionally in small numbers at other places but the largest wintering flock is in Bournemouth Bay where numbers may exceed 1,000. Velvet scoters and long-tailed duck are uncommon and only irregular visitors.

Brent geese occur occasionally in small numbers along the Hampshire coast but the main flocks are found in the harbours and will be mentioned later. Along the Dorset coast geese are scarce and sporadic in occurrence. They are sometimes recorded from the Fleet, that large expanse of coastal water behind the Chesil Beach. This locality has very large winter rafts of wigeon with smaller numbers of other duck such as pintail, golden-eye with occasional gadwall, scaup and smew. At Abbotsbury on the western end of the Fleet is a famous swannery, known to have been in use as early as the fourteenth century. The breeding birds of the coast are much more limited: the human population ensures that. Shelduck are found in various places along the coast where there are suitable nest sites. Small numbers of redshank, oyster-catcher and ringed plover breed on the Hampshire coast and the last named species on the Chesil Beach.

Common, little and sandwich terns nest along the Hampshire coast among the black-headed gull colonies. Hurst spit has been for long a locality for little terns but human pressure has now become too great. Common and little terns breed along the Chesil Beach opposite Abbotsbury and enjoy a measure of protection. A pair of arctic terns once nested here. Roseate terns have bred irregularly in Dorset over a number of years but it was not until 1959 that breeding was proved in Hampshire.

South coast dunes

Where conditions are suitable, for example, where a large area of sand is exposed to on-shore winds, sand dunes may be formed. The gradual formation of this habitat affords a fascinating botanical study as it proceeds from a tiny heap of sand trapped in a clump of sea couch-grass *Agropyron junceiforme*, through the establishment of a long line of foredunes, to mobile dunes with their open community of marram grass *Ammophila arenaria* and then finally to fixed dunes with intervening marshy hollows bearing a great variety of maritime and inland plants. The developing plant succession occurs over a relatively short period of time.

On the Hampshire coast dunes are very poorly represented. They exist generally only in incipient form in a few places. At Hayling Island they support sea holly *Eryngium maritimum*, sea bindweed *Calystegia soldanella*, and such uncommon plants as teesdalia *Teesdalia nudicaulis*, sea lyme-grass *Elymus arenarius*, bulbous meadow-grass *Poa bulbosa* and sand timothy-grass *Phleum arenarium*. The Hampshire Naturalists' Trust maintains a small reserve here to protect the rare *Centaurium littorale* in what is reported to be its only station in southern England. Here grows also the round-leaved cranesbill *Geranium rotundifolium* and the dotted-fruited sedge *Carex punctata*. Portland spurge *Euphorbia portlandica* reaches its most easterly station in Britain at Hayling Island. In the barren and inhospitable habitat of the dunes plants survive by sending down exceptionally long roots and specimens of Portland spurge have been found with roots nearly 4ft long although the above-ground parts are comparatively small.

More extensive dunes occur along the Dorset coast. Those on the eastern side of Poole Harbour at Sandbanks are now largely built over, but on the western side at South Haven Peninsula behind Shell Bay are remarkably fine dune formations, now a National Nature Reserve. These were the subject of detailed surveys by Captain C. Diver in the 1930s. The foreshore plants consist chiefly of orache *Atriplex* spp with sea sandwort *Honckenya peploides* and sea rocket *Cakile maritima*; marram and lyme-grass form the dominant constituents of the dunes immediately behind. The slacks between the ridges have marsh communities which include a white variety of the marsh gentian *Gentiana*

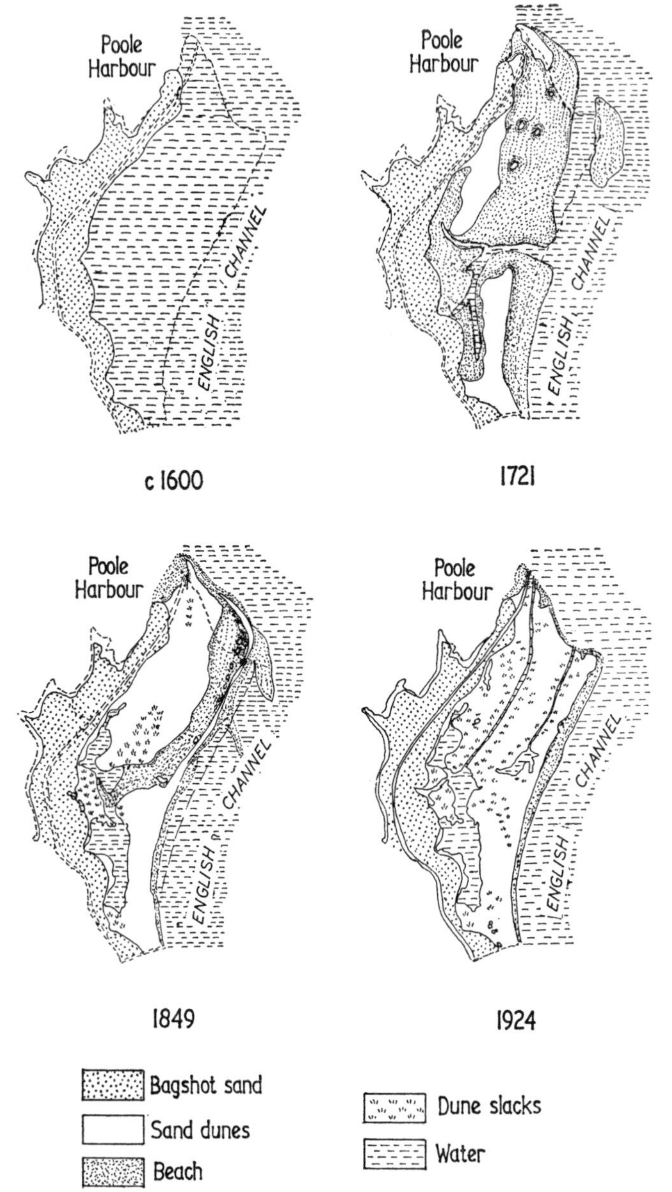

Maps showing the formation of Littlesea, Studland, over 300 years. After Macan and Worthington from *Life in Lakes and Rivers* with permission of Collins, publishers

pneumonanthe and specimens of the royal fern *Osmunda regalis*. Further inland, due to their low calcium content, the oldest dunes have developed into dune-heath dominated by ling *Calluna vulgaris*. A rich lichen community shows distinctive differences in component species between the marram areas and the acidic heath.

Sand dunes have their own typical fauna. Marram grass stems are the pabulum for the shore wainscot *Leucana littoralis*, a moth found commonly in the summer months but only in the vicinity of its sole food plant. Another marram feeder, the sand dart, mentioned earlier as a moth of the shore, is found also on the sand hills. A widely-distributed micromoth on dunes is *Anerastia lotella*, the larvae of which are also marram feeders. The archer's dart *Agrotis vestigialis*, an attractively patterned grey-green moth, is common at Hayling Island and elsewhere. This locality also has a sizeable population of the oblique striped *Mesotype virginata*, the larvae of which feed on lady's bedstraw *Gallium verum*. This plant of course also commonly grows on dry chalk banks, but the moth is decidedly scarce on the chalk uplands of Hampshire, indicating that there must be another factor which links it with the sea coast. The coast dart *Euxo cursoaria* is a moth of northern distribution but within the region it has been found on Dorset dunes. The Portland moth *Actebia praecox* is also found on the sand hills of Dorset but not on the cliffs of Portland; hence its English name is misleading. A common day-flying moth is the six-spot burnet *Zygaena filipendulae* whose caterpillars feed on various leguminous plants. Numbers of butterflies, 'blues' and 'browns', may be seen on sunny days. The caterpillars of the brown argus *Aricia agestis* feed on stork's-bill *Erodium cicutarium*. The acidic dunes of Studland have butterflies of the heath such as the grayling *Eumenis semele*.

Beetles typical of coastal sand-hills include the maritime form of the tiger beetle *Cicindela hybrida*, the local species *Euchlora dubia*, which is of variable but vivid coloration, and a black weevil *Otiorrhynchus atroapterus*. The wood tiger beetle *Cicindela sylvatica* has been recorded in recent years from the Studland acidic dunes. Lesser cockroaches *Ectobius panzeri* are present on the coasts of Hampshire and Dorset, particularly on sand dunes such as those of the Studland reserve.

Numerous species of plant bugs feed on the dune plants, some being specific to particular flowers. Of those that feed on the true coastal plants mention may be made of *Dicranocephalus agilis*, which feeds mainly on the fruit of Portland spurge, and two marram feeders, *Trigonotylus psammaecolor*, which within the region has been recorded only from Hampshire, and the descriptively named bishop's mitre *Aelia acuminata*, a dusky yellow species seen in August.

A small spider particularly associated with dunes is *Philodromus fallax*, whose pale sandy coloration perfectly matches the ground on which it runs. A curiosity of this spider is that the male matures in the spring and is not seen after the end of April whereas the female becomes adult a little later and is present during the early part of the summer. Another Arachnid occurring on sand-hills belongs to that curious family the false-scorpions about which so little is known. It was in fact many years before I even saw one but one day by chance I noticed on a pane of glass a fly which flew off with two tiny creatures clinging to its legs. I thought at first that they were tiny spiders but later learnt that they must have been a species of false-scorpion which makes a habit of hitch-hiking. The coastal species is *Dactylochelifer latreillei*, 2–3mm long and rather strangely lacking the camouflage of the sand dune spider, being dark in colour.

Birds are few in number. The typical bird of the open marram community is the skylark. Where rabbit burrows exist there may be nesting shelduck, as at Studland where the dune heath has introduced such characteristic heathland species as meadow pipit, stonechat and linnet.

An extensive lagoon known as Littlesea, fringed with swampy birch and willow carr, exists within the Studland dune complex. The observation post overlooking the lake is a fine place from which to watch the large numbers of wildfowl which winter here, although a telescope is more useful than binoculars. These birds include whooper and Bewick swans, pochard, tufted duck, golden-eye, shoveler, mallard, wigeon and sometimes a few long-tailed duck and scaup.

Sand lizards and their predators the smooth snakes live in the heather communities; in fact, one of the remarkable features of the Studland reserve is that all six species of the British reptiles live here. Of the mammals, in addition to the rabbits already mentioned, woodmice are abundant, as indicated by the frequent tracks in the sand quite close to the beach. Shrews are common and the little harvest mouse has been seen. This last, contrary to its name and even some accounts of its distribution, is not confined to cornfields. Dunes are a favourite haunt of foxes, and in the birch woods on the Studland reserve live roe deer.

It should be mentioned that as the whole of this area was bombarded with live shells during World War II, as a dress rehearsal for the invasion of the continent, care is still advisable.

Salt marshes of the south coast

The word 'saltings' indicates at once the outstanding and overriding chemical factor which determines the nature of the flora of the coastal marshes. Although the conditions are stringent, a number of species have adapted themselves to this habitat. At the lowest level, grasswrack or eel-grass *Zostera marina* waves its long green ribbons in the flowing tide. This plant, a favourite food of brent geese, has become much rarer than it used to be but still grows at various places including Hayling Island, Calshot and even the brackish water lagoon of the Fleet, behind the Chesil Beach.

Samphire is a confusing word which is used of three different and unrelated coastal plants. It is therefore preferable to use the name glasswort instead of marsh samphire for *Salicornia europaea*, which is a coloniser of mud in the zone above *Zostera*. This is a common, sometimes abundant, plant of the salt marsh, and a number of rarer species occur which are difficult to dis-

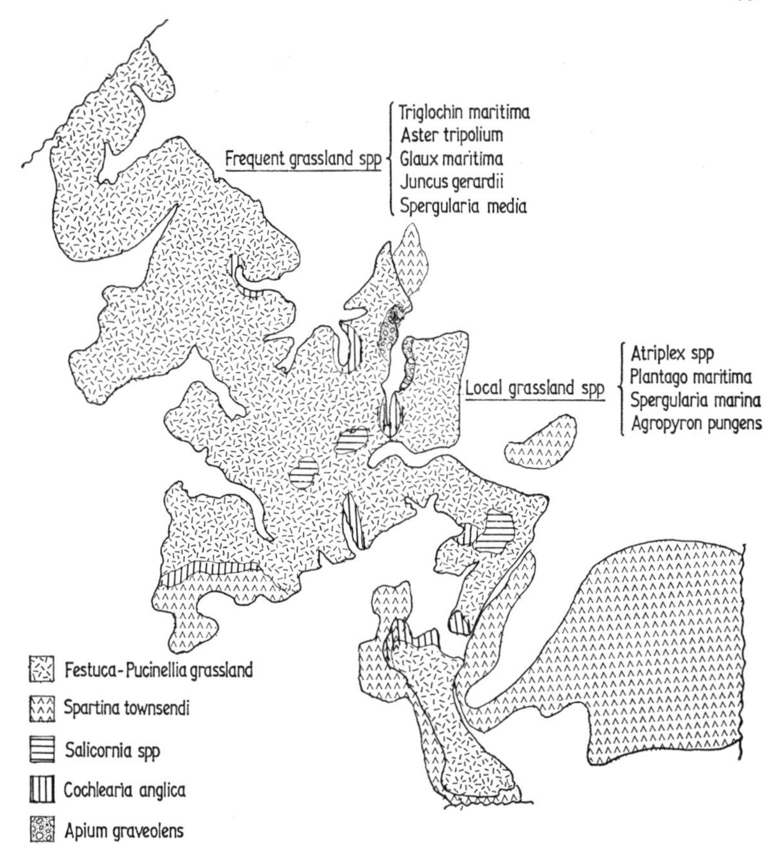

Eling Great Marsh showing principal salt-marsh plant communities. Simplified sketch based on Bowman. Not to scale

tinguish from each other. Also in this zone are the sea blite *Suaeda maritima* and the sea aster *Aster tripolium* which are common in both counties. At the head of Southampton Water the plant communities of Eling Great Marsh are typical of the southern coastline.

Another and overwhelmingly successful coloniser of mud is the hybrid cord-grass *Spartina townsendii*. The origin of this plant is not certain but it is believed to be a hybrid between *S. maritima* and *S. alternifolia*. The former is the native British species and the latter is an American species which appeared in Southampton Water in 1836. This estuary is the type locality for the hybrid which was discovered at Hythe on the western shore of Southampton Water in 1870 and named after the author of the *Flora of Hampshire*. This vigorous and larger plant has spread tremendously; by 1899 it had reached Poole Harbour. It is now widespread and because of its stabilising ability it has been introduced to mudflats to help reclaim land. It has practically eliminated the other two species, although at Marchwood a colony of *S. alternifolia* still survives. The statement that the hybrid is vigorous should perhaps be qualified for in recent years there has been a certain amount of die-back. It was first observed at Beaulieu in 1930 and has happened since at various places along the Hampshire coast. The phenomenon is being studied by workers from Southampton university. It seems that it is not due either to pollution or disease but probably to certain unknown chemical factors.

Cord grass usually grows in a community from which it has excluded most other plants but in the salt marsh at higher levels above the *Spartina* there is an association of salt-tolerating species. Typical members include sea lavender *Limonium vulgare*, sea arrow-grass *Triglochin maritima*, sea spurrey *Spergularia marina*, the sea rushes *Juncus gerardii* and *J. maritima*, sea milkwort *Glaux maritima* and salt-marsh grass *Puccinellia maritima*. *Limonium humile* is an uncommon sea lavender which grows at Needs Oar at the mouth of the Beaulieu river and at a few other places on the Hampshire coast but is not recorded from Dorset. On Park Shore, west of the Beaulieu estuary, and at a few places elsewhere grows the uncommon but locally abundant Borrer's salt-marsh grass *P. fasciculata*. The uncommon annual beard-grass *Polypogon monspeliensis* and the very rare perennial beard-grass *Agropogon littoralis* grow on the Hampshire Naturalists' Trust reserve at Farlington Marshes.

Certain plants grow in the transition zone of brackish water between the salt-marsh proper and fresh-water swamp. These include the water dropwort *Oenanthe lachenalii*, a species which throughout the country is not very common but within the region is fairly frequent in brackish grassland at such widely separated places as Farlington Marshes and Poole Harbour; the sea club rushes *Scirpus maritimus* and *S. tabernaemontani* are frequent in brackish grassland and salt-marsh pools; two uncommon plants of the buttercup family *Ranunculus baudotii* and *R. sardous* occur infrequently in this habitat in both counties. Amongst the grasses sea barley *Hordeum marinum* and sea couch *Agropyron pungens* are typical of salt-marsh margins.

Salt-marshes are rich in animal life, some of it specific to this habitat; they seem, however, to be rather neglected by the naturalist, probably because of the difficulties of access and the uncongenial nature of the terrain. Without a doubt, much remains to be discovered here in the realm of animal ecology. *Spartina* beds a mile or more off-shore have been found in various places in England to have blue tits, harvest mice, bank voles and weasels.

Typical moths of the Hampshire coastal marshes are the dog's tooth *Hadena suasa*, the saltern form of the ear moth *Hydraecia paludis*, and Matthew's wainscot *Leucania favicolor*. A micro-moth which is locally abundant on sea lavender is *Agdistis bennetii*. Larvae of the star-wort *Cucillia asteris* feed on the flowers of sea aster in both counties.

The locally distributed grasshopper *Chorthippus albomarginatus* is recorded as common in the saltings of Poole Harbour and at Lodmoor near Weymouth, where are varieties of grasshopper including the cricket of the saltings, *Conocephalus dorsalis*. A number of species of plant bugs inhabit the salt marshes. A tiny red capsid bug *Orthotylus rabidus* lives in the glasswort zone, its colour matching the red tinge of the plant stems in autumn. Another species of this genus, *O. moncreiffi* feeds on sea purslane. A capsid *Conostethus frisicus* which feeds on sea lavender on the northern and eastern coasts has been recorded from the south coast only in Dorset. Two species of *Teratocornis* live on the sea club rush and glaucous rush growing in salt-water pools. A southern continental bug *Saldula setulosa* was discovered in the higher levels of Poole Harbour saltings in 1904, and presumably feeds on cord-grass.

Mention has already been made of harvest mice occurring on the sand dunes of Studland, and another colony was discovered in recent years on Farlington Marshes.

The beds of *Spartina* at Needs Oar at the mouth of the Beaulieu river and along the coast to Hurst Castle hold large breeding colonies of black-headed gulls which have increased spectacularly in recent years. In 1970 over 17,000 pairs of these nested at Needs Oar. The long-established egg collecting, which is still permitted under control in the early part of the breeding season, has clearly had no adverse effect. Although the breeding of little, common and sandwich terns is subject to fluctuations, numbers in general have also increased. The common terns often nest in the communities of sea purslane which occupy a well marked linear zone on the edge of the *Spartina*.

It is now generally known that in the last few years a few Mediterranean black-headed gulls have summered at Needs Oar and breeding has been proved. A bird was first observed in 1966 and nesting is known to have taken place in 1968. It should be mentioned that this whole area is wardened and kept strictly private. It is in the best interests of the birds that bird-watchers should keep away in the hope that this new species will establish itself. This spot is a favourite locality for spotted redshank, which occur in numbers up to seventy in the autumn, and smaller numbers over-winter.

The salt-marsh pasture behind Farlington sea wall has nesting pairs of yellow wagtails, lapwing and redshank. Out of the breeding season large flocks of curlew and black-tailed godwit use the fields as a high-tide roost, and I have even seen on one occasion a flock of golden plover. Various birds of prey including harriers, short-eared owls and peregrine occasionally hunt the marshes. The *Phragmites* fringing the large pool here often holds a spotted crake in the early autumn, and I have watched a migrating black tern hawking over the water in October. I have seen, too, incredibly, a Franklyn's gull bathing itself in the water here, the first record for Britain. A flock of twites are fairly regular winter visitors and at one time or another many rarities have been recorded from these marshes.

In the marshes at Titchfield Haven bearded tits and jack snipe are winter visitors. The bittern and even the little bittern are also occasionally recorded. A Cetti's warbler spent a month here in the spring of 1961; attention was first drawn to it by the unusual song coming from the depths of thick reeds, and it was eventually identified by mist-netting.

The Pennington Marshes are another rewarding spot for bird-watchers. A great grey shrike often winters here; kingfishers are frequently seen; garganey visit the pools in spring and rarer birds such as pectoral sandpiper and Sabine's gull have been observed from time to time.

Estuaries and harbours of the south coast

Strictly speaking, the word 'estuary' has a topographical connotation rather than an ecological one for it covers a combination of habitats, but nevertheless there are some distinctive features which are worth listing in a section of their own.

The eastern boundaries of the region include the western part of Chichester Harbour. Here in winter a sizeable flock of dark-breasted brent geese can be seen. A larger flock, which in 1970 exceeded 3,000 birds, winters in the adjacent Langstone Harbour although probably some interchange takes place between the two flocks. There has been a spectacular increase in the numbers of this species at Langstone in the last few years, the maximum in 1966 for example was less than half this figure. This harbour is now the main locality for brent geese on the south coast and one or two birds of the light-breasted race have even been seen at Langstone. If, as now seems certain, the third London airport is sited at Foulness, it is probable that the brent population might then move to Langstone, but there is evidence that the average wintering numbers there reached their peak several years ago and it is very doubtful if the area could absorb any more.

Wigeon and shelduck are perhaps the most numerous of the duck at Langstone. The banked up waters of the river Meon behind the sluice gates at Titchfield Haven is another good place for waterfowl; I have even seen on a spring day a red-throated diver swimming quite tamely a few yards from the bridge, undisturbed by passing traffic.

Going westward we come to the drowned river valley of Southampton Water. Near its mouth it is entered by the Hamble river which is tidal as far inland as Botley. Along the lower reaches occur the littoral shells, Baltic tellin and edible sand gaper, both species able to tolerate the lower salinities of estuaries. Further up Southampton Water in the estuary of the river Itchen, a rare species of those strange molluscs the sea hares can be found.

As might be expected, the waste ground in and around Southampton docks has a varied alien flora. Conspicuous outside the west gate of the New Docks is a society of Verlot's mugwort *Artemisia verlotorum*. This is a Far Eastern plant which arrived in France in 1873 from south-west China and has now reached England.

In recent years several alien species of marine life have not only established themselves but have spread beyond the estuary. The commonest barnacle now in Southampton Water is an Australian species *Elminius modestus*, which did not arrive in England until the 1940s but has now spread along the south coast and is moving northwards. A large mollusc of eastern North America, the hard-shell clam *Mercenaria mercenaria*, was first recorded from Southampton Water in 1957 when a few specimens were probably thrown overboard from an American ship. It is now estimated that there are up to 1,000 small clams per square yard at Marchwood. This is an edible species and a local industry has developed as a consequence, the majority being exported to France. Oyster fisheries died out twenty years ago, but recently a large new bed of an estimated 9 million oysters has been found. In the same year a minute American copepod *Acartia tonsa* was first discovered in this country in Southampton Water. On the eastern side at Weston shore and at other places along the coast, including Poole Harbour, lives the American piddock *Petricola pholadiformis*, a bivalve which arrived in this country about the beginning of the century. A plant bug, *Saldula palustris*, was first identified from Southampton Water specimens last century. The larvae are found in the lower part of *Spartina* clumps and can tolerate submersion by the tide. The warm water outfall already referred to not only provides an ideal niche for lower forms of marine life but is also an attractive place for fish and birds. Shoals of mullet and bass are found here and a flock of golden-eye are probably attracted by the rich fare in the shape of crustaceans and molluscs. Dibden Bay on the west side has for some time been well watched by ornithologists, but the reclaiming of the mudflats has lessened its attractiveness. Roesel's bush cricket *Metrioptera roeselii*, an East Anglian insect, has an isolated outpost in grassland bordering Southampton Water.

Christchurch Harbour is the estuary formed by the confluence of the rivers Avon and Stour. A sand bar stretches eastwards from Hengistbury Head and restricts the mouth of the estuary to a very narrow fast-running channel at Mudeford. Until 1911 the mouth was a mile to the east towards Highcliffe, but in November of that year the water broke through the sand bar. There is a well-known run of salmon at this spot. The harbour is a good spot for birds; I have seen Kentish plover and grey phalarope here. White wagtails are often seen in the spring, and spoonbills are occasional visitors in the early autumn. The flowering rush *Butomus umbellatus* is an uncommon plant in Hampshire, but it is found here and at Titchfield Haven as well as at a few other places.

Poole Harbour holds a considerable population of golden-eye and red-breasted merganser in winter, with smaller numbers of scaup, pintail and long-tailed duck. There are a number of islands in the harbour, of which by far the most important from a natural history point of view is Brownsea. This island is owned by the National Trust, but part is leased to the Dorset County Naturalists' Trust. A previous owner had let nature run riot, so that rhododendrons became a jungle obliterating the tracks and rats rampaged unchecked. Clearance work still remains to be done, although progress has been made.

Scenically the island is most picturesque, with lakes, a brackish lagoon and mature conifers including much maritime pine *Pinus pinaster* with some Monterey pine *P. radiata* as well as the native Scots pine *P. sylvestris*. Red squirrels inhabit the plantations where sika deer were once found, though none of these have been seen since the 1940s. Among the pines is a heronry, one of the largest in the British Isles. The tame peacocks are a colourful feature of life on Brownsea. The two lakes have so far proved disappointing, attracting few wildfowl apart from the resident Canada Geese. The coastal lagoon is more rewarding, and here in most winters one or two avocets can be seen, an extremely rare species along the coast of the region, with a variety of other waders and duck sometimes including numbers of the elegant pintail. The common tern has begun breeding on the island.

Further west, at Weymouth, is Radipole Lake. This in the last century was the estuary of the small river Wey, and open to seagoing vessels. Now it is a dammed-up backwater of the river and consists of several reedy lagoons. As long ago as 1928 it was made a local bird sanctuary and is now also designated a Site of Special Scientific Interest. The area is very close to the centre of the town and building development may seriously affect its proven value as a bird reserve. Pintail, pochard, tufted duck, shoveler, mallard and teal occur in numbers, and severe weather brings in merganser, scaup and smew. This is probably the best place on the south coast for little gulls, and black terns are not only regular autumn visitors but increasing in numbers. Bitterns are occasionally seen in winter and bearded tits have moved into the locality in recent years. One of my memorable birding experiences is of standing hidden in reeds which reached well above my head whilst a small flock of bearded tits chattered all around me unconcerned.

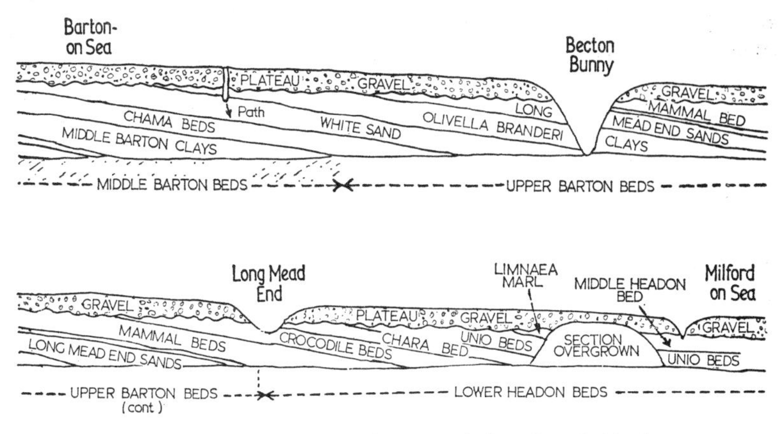

Diagrammatic section of Barton cliffs. After Shelford

Cliffs

The fame of Hampshire's cliffs must rest not on their flora and fauna but on their fossils. The five mile stretch of Barton cliffs is the type locality for the Barton Beds with their abundant fossil record of life in early Tertiary times. More than 500 species have been identified here. In these marine sediments there are many species of mollusca, including numerous turret shells and lamellibranchs such as *Chama squamosa* and *Corbula* spp. Sharks' teeth are fairly plentiful in the Middle Barton, and above the Barton the Headon strata contain crocodile, mammal and leaf beds although mammal remains are nowadays difficult to find. This whole line of cliff is unstable and cliff falls are frequent. This can give the fossil hunter opportunity to examine new areas but care should be taken in view of the dangerous state of the cliffs. On the uneven slopes there are also areas of treacherous sticky blue clay which should be avoided. The whole area provides an instructive occasion to observe various incipient forms of geological structure such as mud flows, clay pellet formation and slide planes.

At Highcliffe, on the terraces, moist hollows on impermeable

Middle Headon Beds

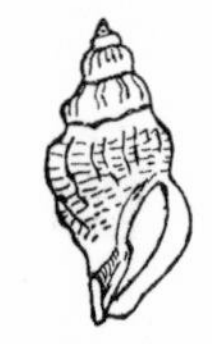

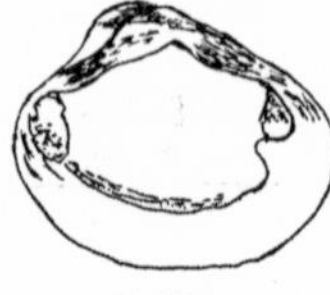

Lower Headon Beds

Upper Barton Beds

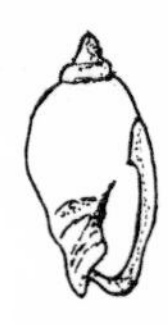

Middle Barton Beds

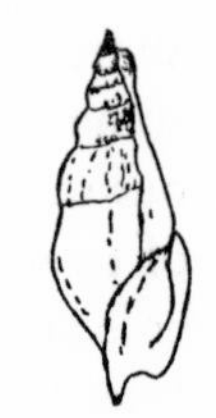

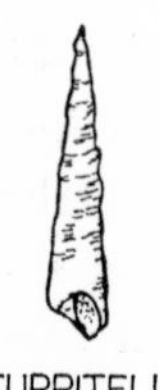

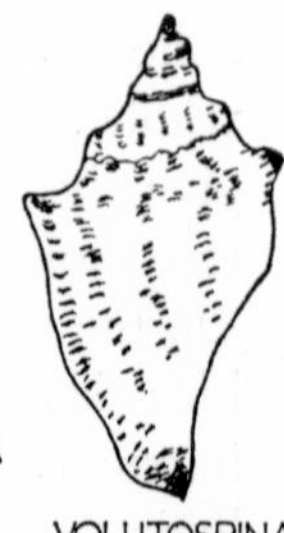

A selection of Barton cliff fossils. After Shelford

Page 53 (*above*) Durleigh reservoir near Bridgwater—haunt of duck and waders; (*below*) purple loosestrife, figwort and willow herb on the banks of the river Itchen

Page 54 (*above*) Protesting coot on the Kennet & Avon canal with guelder rose behind; (*below*) leaping salmon on the river Test

clay contain aquatic plants such as *Typha latifolia* and here can be found an uncommon plant bug *Saldula arenicola* which in Britain is confined to a few southern counties. Here, too, in this habitat is the fly with the largest wing-span in Britain, *Tipula maxima*, the dragonfly *Libellula depressa* and the bulrush wainscot moth *Nonagria typhae.*

Hengistbury Head is a massive promontory of Bracklesham Beds guarding the western side of Christchurch Harbour. Ironstone has been mined here in the past. The area of concretionary boulders at the base of the cliff is a place where purple sandpipers have on infrequent occasions been seen. The cliff top has communities of ling *Calluna vulgaris* and gorse *Ulex europaeus.* The natterjack toad *Bufo calamita* used to occur here but there have not apparently been any records in recent years. During the first thirty years of the century the l-album wainscot *Leucania l-album* was an extremely rare moth—it was not discovered in Britain until 1910—but in recent years it has become common in its favoured localities of sheltered promontories such as Hengistbury, Studland and Swanage. The headland at Hengistbury is a good migration point and a ringing station is maintained here.

The Dorset cliffs are much more extensive and of great interest. The rocks range from the Blue Lias at the base of the Jurassic at Lyme Regis, with their fossil oysters, reptile bones and ammonites, to the Bagshot Sand cliffs at Studland with their imprints of the leaves of tropical plants. An abundant and distinctive fossil in the disused quarries of Portland is *Aptyxiella portlandica*, known locally as the Portland screw. At Lulworth on a cliff ledge high above the sea is a striking fossil forest. The access on the eastern side of the cove is not very conspicuous and one day a small group I was leading, or rather misleading, became almost stranded on slippery cliffs at the point. When I did finally discover the steep marshy path to the top it was worth the effort in more ways than one, for the remote hidden ledge was a sun trap whilst on the shingle beach in the cove holiday-makers were huddled in warm clothing.

A remarkable natural phenomenon occurred in the last century on the cliff between Ringstead Bay and the White Nothe headland. In the year 1826 a man was digging in his garden near the cliff top when his spade fell into a hole of burning shale in the beds of Kimmeridge Clay. Clouds of smoke emerged and then the cliff face burst into blue flames. This continued for about a year, making a tourist attraction for Weymouth, and the shales continued to smoulder for some four years, the rocks above being baked almost to tiles in the process. It was rapid oxidisation of iron pyrites which had set the oil shales alight. The cliffs between Lyme Regis and Charmouth similarly caught fire in 1751 and again in 1908.

In summer some of the cliff sections are colourful with clumps of thrift *Armeria maritima*, scurvy-grass *Cochlearia officinalis*, and kidney vetch *Anthyllis vulneraria*. Samphire *Crithmum maritumum*, golden samphire *Inula crithmoides*, wild cabbage *Brassica oleracea*, rock sea lavender *Limonium binervosum* and the Portland spurge *Euphorbia portlandica*, although relatively common, are more restricted in distribution. The promontory of Portland is particularly rich in cliff species. The red valerian *Centranthus ruber* is abundant. In addition to the samphires and the Portland spurge already mentioned there are the early flowering Danish scurvy-grass *Cochlearia danica*, sea carrot *Daucus gummifer*, rock sea spurrey *Spergularia rupicola* and a very rare plant only found here, the Portland sea lavender *Limonium recurvum*.

The tops of the calcareous cliffs of Dorset are naturally rich in flowers. The following selection of plants growing in the vicinity of Durlston Head, Swanage, is indicative of the variety:

wild carrot	*Daucus carota*
wild thyme	*Thymus serpyllus*
buckshorn plantain	*Plantago coronopus*
hoary plantain	*Plantago media*
yellow centaury	*Blackstonia perfoliata*
purging flax	*Linum catharticum*
salad burnet	*Poterium sanguisorba*

sea campion	*Silene maritima*
bee orchid	*Ophrys apifera*
early spider orchid	*Ophrys sphegodes*

The high proportion of calcicolous plants is at once noticeable. Perhaps the most interesting plant in the list is the early spider orchid which is highly characteristic of limestone coastal downs in Dorset. Indeed, this county is now one of the main strongholds of this orchid whose area of distribution is shrinking.

These limestone cliff grasslands are good places for butterflies, including the green hairstreak *Callophrys rubi* and at least four species of blues, the common *Polyommatus icarus*, the small *Cupido minimus*, the holly *Celastrina argiolus* and the adonis *Lysandra bellargus*. They are also good places to look for the occasional rare migrant butterfly or the swarms of clouded yellows *Colius croceus* which occur in some years. To lepidopterists Lulworth Cove is noteworthy for the Lulworth skipper *Thymelicus acteon*, a butterfly first discovered in the early part of last century near the cove and subsequently found to occur along the coast between Weymouth and the Isle of Purbeck and at a few places in Devon. It is thus very restricted in distribution and confined to the coast though this does not apply to this species on the continent. The caterpillar feeds on grasses and is believed to favour the slender brome *Bromus lepidus*.

A number of moths are typical of coastal cliffs, particularly the limestone ones. The larvae of the six-belted clearwing *Dipsosphecia scopegira* thrive on the kidney vetch and the more common birdsfoot trefoil *Lotus corniculatus*. The caterpillars of the galium carpet *Epirrhoe galeata* live, as the name implies, on bedstraw and are common on coastal limestone. The wormwood moth *Cucullia absinthia* is a species of south-western distribution, the larvae feeding on the flowers of sea wormwood *Artemisia maritima*. It occurs at Portland but recently has spread to Hampshire where it is being seen in towns, the food plant in this case probably being the common wormwood *A. vulgaris*. The feathered brindle *Aporophyla australis*, feathered ranunculus

Eumichtis lichenea and Portland ribbon wave *Sterrha degeneraria* are other local species which exist at Portland.

Amongst the micromoths may be mentioned *Agdistis staticus* which within the region occurs only on Dorset cliffs, the caterpillars feeding on the leaves of rock sea lavender. The common Pyralid moth *Scoparia mercuria* has a local sub-species *portlandica* on Portland. Another much more local species on the Dorset coast is *Dolicharthra punctalis* which does however occur also in Somerset and the Isle of Wight.

The grasshopper *Stenobothrus lineatus* is not generally a very common species but is reported to be common at St Aldhelms Head and no doubt occurs at other places along the Dorset cliffs. In the vicinity of Portland Bill four species have been recorded: the two common *Chorthippus* species *C. parallelus* and *C. brunneus*, the great green grasshopper *Tettigonia viridissima* and the grey bush cricket *Platycleis denticulata*, a distinctly maritime species in England and found only along the south coast although on the continent it is much more widely distributed.

The Hampshire cliffs do not hold populations of cliff-breeding birds; even the rock pipit has become only a spasmodic breeder. Ravens nested regularly on Hengistbury Head until the end of World War II but they do so no longer. Dorset is rather more fortunate in cliff birds although certain localities are more favoured than others. Jackdaws and herring gulls are now well distributed along the cliffs but a Burton Bradstock fisherman claims that it was only after World War I that the last named bird came to nest on the cliffs of that part of the coast. Ravens nest in a few places and the rock pipit is a fairly common breeder.

The Durlston Head–St Aldhelms Head section and the promontory of Portland are the best areas for sea birds. Among the auks there are numbers of guillemots with much lesser numbers of razorbills and puffins. Kittiwakes breed and fulmars are present throughout the summer at both places. In the holm oaks at Durlston an American brown thrasher lived for several weeks in 1967, the first occurrence in the British Isles and only the second European record. It was a great thrill to stand on the cliff-top only four feet from the bird as with its curved bill it foraged amongst the dead leaves under the tamarisk bushes.

Another recent astonishing rarity was the wallcreeper which arrived at Winspit in the autumn of 1969 and spent the winter on the rock face. This was only the seventh record for the British Isles. It is just slightly larger than its common woodland relative and difficult to locate, but when found the crimson, black and white spotted wings and the upside-down walking on cave roofs make it a memorable experience.

Portland is an exceptionally good area for bird-watching and many rarities have been reported from there. Ring ouzels, fire-crests and black redstarts are regular in autumn, the first on the steep scrub-covered slopes of the Verne and the last two in the old quarries. Names like woodchat shrike, pallas, parula and desert warblers, lapland and ortolan buntings, red-breasted fly-catchers, tawny and olive-backed pipits are mouth-watering to the naturalist and all have been observed at Portland. The Bill is good also for sea watching, and species such as storm and Leach's petrels, divers, skuas and shearwaters of several species can be seen here.

The Somerset coast

Part of the Somerset coast has been covered by another book in this series *The Naturalist in Devon and Cornwall.* We are concerned here only with the coastline east of the Quantocks to the county boundary at Portishead at the mouth of the Avon where the brackish waters of the Severn estuary merge with the sea water of the Bristol Channel. The length of coast under consideration must therefore be counted as marine rather than estuarine, but such a distinction is to a large extent arbitrary, and marine species in fact begin to decline from the Somerset–Devon border eastwards.

The Bristol Channel, the largest inlet of the sea in Britain, is a drowned river valley formed by ancient tectonic movement as a hollow in the earth's crust; there are indications of its existence 300 million years ago and it underwent its first submergence some 140 million years later. Subsequently it became the estuary of a river flowing in the reverse direction from the present one, and in the period when the Chalk deposits were being formed underwent a further subsidence. By the end of the Tertiary era the depression was occupied by a west flowing river as at the present day.

Although the stretch of coast within our purview is only some forty miles or so, the habitat types run the gamut of mudflats, salt-marshes, sandy beaches, dunes, and there is even a little shingle.

The Berrow Flats, Weston Bay and Sand Bay are sandy shores. Sea couch grass is common along the strand and in places sand sedge *Carex arenaria* is frequent. The shore crab *Carcinus maenas* is abundant. Amongst the molluscs, mention can be made of the Baltic tellin *Macoma balthica* which is very plentiful on the shore, and thoroughly at home in the muddy waters of low saline content. A large and rather local ground beetle of sandy shores with a distribution confined to the South West is *Eurynebia complanata*. This Carabid is mainly yellow in colour with black markings on the elytra and is found on the shore at Burnham. Amongst the moths are the sand dart and the feathered brindle, the larvae of the latter feeding on sea campion. Of the wading birds, numbers of curlew, redshank and dunlin are to be seen out of the breeding season and sanderling is a passage-migrant, a small number of them wintering between Burnham and Brean.

Shingle deposits are scarce but they have formed an extensive bar at the entrance to the Parrett estuary extending towards Steart Island, another accumulation of shingle. A belt of shingle lies behind the sandy shore of Sand Bay. Agates, originating from the Old Red Sandstone cliffs north of Clevedon, can sometimes be found amongst the beach pebbles. In the Steart Point area and on Steart Island well-rounded balls of blue clay dotted with small pebbles sometimes appear on the tide-line. This phenomenon appears to be due to the cutting up by wave action of an exposed bed of clay and the subsequent rounding of fragments by the rapid currents. Small numbers of oyster-catchers and ringed plover nest on the shingle ridges but no terns now breed. Herring and lesser black-backed gulls began breeding on Steart Island during World War II and the former have now established a large colony.

From Burnham sand dunes stretch through Berrow five miles north to Brean Down. They are most developed in the southern part where they extend inland for perhaps half to three-quarters of a mile. There is the inevitable marram and also sea lyme grass, soapwort *Saponaria officinalis*, evening primrose *Oenothera biennis*, spring vetch *Vicia lathyroides*, a variety of the dog violet *Viola canina* var. *macratha*, musky stork's bill *Erodium moschatum* and gladdon *Iris foetidissima*, which last species is especially typical of Somerset dunes. Strong clumps of sea buckthorn *Hippophae rhamnoides* grow at the rear of the dunes, the berries providing food in late autumn and winter for numbers of thrushes and finches. In the slacks between the ridges grow marsh helleborine *Epipactis palustris*, the round-headed sea rush *Scirpus holoschoenus*, found only in one or two other British localities, and a common moss of marshy ground, *Acrocladium cuspidatum*, with bright green spear-tipped branches.

The moths include sand dart and the white colon *Heliophobus albicolon*, the larvae of which feeds on a variety of low-growing plants. A plant bug, *Arenocoris fallini*, feeds on the stork's bill, and another bug, *Hallodapus montandoni*, occurs here but nowhere else in the region. Birds which nest on the dunes are skylark, meadow pipit, shelduck and various warblers and finches.

Salt-marshes exist in various places, notably at the river estuaries. The composition of these marshes is similar to those described in the section on the south coast. *Spartina townsendii* has formed extensive communities, although it was not planted until 1928. Snipe, redshank, mallard and shelduck breed on these marshes, and a summer visitor, the yellow wagtail, roosts here.

At the mouth of the river Parrett in Bridgwater Bay there are 20 square miles of mudflats, where the ragworm *Nereis diversicolor* is abundant. Large flocks of curlew, redshank, dunlin and knot winter in Bridgwater Bay with smaller numbers of turnstone, black-tailed and bar-tailed godwits. Single avocets occasionally winter here. Geese flocks are relatively small but brent and white-fronts occur. An interesting feature of Bridgwater Bay is that in summer it becomes what is believed to be the only moulting area in Britain for shelduck although it seems that the local shelduck migrate to north-west Germany for this purpose.

Sea anemones do not find congenial conditions along this coastline but in pools on the rocky sections the dahlia anemone *Tealia felina* can be found. A few rock pipits nest along the rocky shores; herring gulls and jackdaws breed on the cliffs and the raven is a rare nester, regularly breeding in only one locality. Samphire grows on ledges and the sea spleenwort *Asplenium marinum* in crevices.

Brean Down, a fine coastal promontory of Carboniferous Limestone, is a westward extension of the Mendips. The slopes are clothed with a shrub layer of elder, hawthorn, bramble and bracken. The herb layer contains the rarities of white rock-rose *Helianthemum apenninum* and hair-grass *Koeleria vallesiana*. This is a haunt of stonechats and linnets, and ring ouzels are seen in autumn. On another limestone outcrop near Weston-super-Mare grows an extremely rare plant, *Linosyris vulgaris*. Further north the Old Red Sandstone cliffs between Clevedon and Portishead contain fossil remains of Devonian fish.

It was on Somerset coastal cliffs a few years ago that I had my most unusual animal encounter. From the beach I heard a scream on the cliffs above. Two mammals were dashing madly through the scrub. Suddenly one of them, a rabbit, came rushing down the slope, over-balanced and turned several somersaults on the rocks. It recovered at once and hurtled along the cliff face at a tremendous pace. I was puzzled until I saw in front of the rabbit the low, lithe form of a stoat running for its life. There was a temporary lull as the rabbit paused on top of a boulder and the stoat then turned and faced its unexpected pursuer. But the truce was over a few seconds later as once again the rabbit chased the stoat back through the hawthorn and up to the top of the cliff out of sight. Almost certainly the rabbit was a female defending her young.

The Bristol dock complex, like other major British ports, has its quota of the black rat *Rattus rattus*, but although its distribution is not confined entirely to dockside habitats it does not appear to be able to spread beyond the boundaries of the city itself. The cargo boats import alien species of animals, particularly invertebrates such as spiders. They are not normally capable of establishing themselves, but *Segestria florentina*, which is considered to be the largest spider in Britain, has been successful in forming thriving colonies in a few coastal towns including Bristol. It lives in the crevices in brickwork and catches its prey by constructing trip lines below the hole. It is significant that this spider occurs also at Bridport on the south coast, a tiny Dorset port which receives visits from small foreign cargo vessels.

Out in the Bristol Channel three and a half miles west of Brean Down lies the uninhabited island of Steep Holm. It is a small outcrop of Carboniferous Limestone only 47 acres in extent, and like Brean Down is an extension of the Mendips. Its highest point is 256ft and the northern part has steep scree-covered cliffs.

Much of the ground is covered with a mixed scrub of elder, blackthorn, sycamore, bramble and privet. On the plateau there are dense communities of the two umbellifers, alexanders *Smyrnium olusatrum* and hemlock *Conium maculatum*. Other plants include the rare wild leek *Allium ampeloprasum*, the golden samphire *Inula crithmoides* and the tree mallow *Lavatera arborea*, the last two both characteristic and locally common species of sea cliffs in the south and west. But the speciality of Steep Holm is the wild paeony *Paeonia mascula* which occurs here in its only British station. These plants, first discovered in 1803, probably originated as garden escapes.

In the scrub growth breed common resident passerines such as robin, wren and blackbird. On the plateau and cliff ledges there are large colonies of gulls, herring, lesser and great black-backed. By far the most abundant is the herring gull, some six times as many as the lesser black-headed which is limited to the plateau, a typical habitat for this species. Cormorants breed but there are no shags or auks. The island is on a migration flight line, and in the autumn small passerines are seen crossing over from the Welsh coast.

CHAPTER THREE

Aquatic habitats

Rivers–Canals–Still waters–Marshland and river margins–Fens

THE GREENNESS OF England, which we take so much for granted, is to visitors from many lands overseas an overwhelming revelation. The land is green, of course, because of the rainfall, but not from this alone. Many parts of Britain have a much higher rainfall but lack a coat of green due to the impermeability of the rock and the rapid run-off. In the lowlands of southern England the modest rainfall is not lost so easily. It sinks into the immense chalk reservoirs bottomed with impermeable strata and there issues forth in innumerable springs, brooks, streams and rivers.

As if these natural waters were not enough man has constructed a large number of dew ponds, village ponds, lakes, reservoirs, gravel pits and a network of canals, which collectively exercise a tremendously beneficial influence on wild life by providing suitable habitats. For nature lovers they not only add greatly to the charm of the countryside but also introduce a considerable variety of specialised plant and animal life.

Rivers

The rivers of Hampshire are mainly chalk streams, that is, most of them rise on the chalk although they have to flow through Tertiary beds for a part of their length before reaching the Solent. The principal ones are the Meon, Itchen and Test.

These chalk streams of southern England have a shallow gradient of 4ft or less per mile and flow through water meadows, now disused but originally intended to increase productivity by periodic flooding. A high-level carrier was taken off the main river and from this numerous branches were constructed at right angles. These ended short of the main river in order to prevent too rapid a run-off; this was effected gradually by drains which intersected the feeders. The silted-up waterways still largely remain, forming valuable marsh habitats.

Another feature of the chalk country is the bourne. Bournes are streams which run intermittently when the water table rises above the level of the river bed. They vary from streams which only disappear at times of drought in high summer to dry valleys which are only flooded in late winter when the springs rise.

Like so much else, the chalk streams are not what they used to be. They have been justly noted for the clarity and purity of the water but according to a river-keeper on the Hampshire Avon a decline can be seen in each successive year. Far too many people use a river as a means of getting rid of unwanted rubbish.

Although the Avon flows through both Hampshire and Wiltshire the greater part of its length is in the latter county. Despite the three major right-bank tributaries of the Ebble, Nadder and Wylye, large areas of Salisbury Plain are waterless. Between the Test and Avon flow the New Forest streams of quite different character, but mention will be made of these in Chapter Eight. The Stour is the longest Dorset river, originating in a complex mass of headwaters north of Shaftesbury and joining the Avon in their Hampshire estuary. The Piddle and Frome are two mainly east-flowing rivers which run closely parallel in their last length as they outfall into Poole Harbour just beyond Wareham. No large rivers breach the Dorset cliffs.

What Berkshire rivers lack in number they make up in size for the mighty Thames forms the northern boundary both of the county and the region. Within the region the principal Thames tributary traversing Wiltshire and Berkshire is the Kennet. Smaller but interesting tributaries are the Pang and Loddon, the latter rising in Hampshire near Basingstoke.

The rivers of Somerset generally flow north-westwards into

the Bristol Channel. They include the Parrett with its numerous headwaters and tributaries, the Brue, the Axe, the Yeo and last but not least, the Bristol Avon. This last named is 75 miles long; both its source and its estuary are in Gloucestershire but during its journey it passes through Wiltshire and Somerset. At the section where it has cut through the Carboniferous Limestone to produce the famous Avon gorge it is spectacular by any standards and for good measure the gorge grows a wealth of rare flowers as well.

Identification of Somerset rivers is made difficult by duplication of names; there are two rivers each of the Axe, the Yeo and the Frome. The Mendips have the underground streams which are so characteristic of limestone country. The northern river Axe is a limestone stream emerging at Wookey; at Henton some five miles or so from its source I have found its rate of flow to be 3ft per second and vegetation is absent; this and similar upper reaches are thus almost within the category of the torrential zone. The famous Severn Bore or tidal wave which occurs twice a day at spring tides of 40ft and upwards in height does not begin until Sharpness in Gloucestershire is reached, but a lesser bore operates on the river Parrett. This and neighbouring rivers flow through the low-lying land of the fens and are subject to floods, although extensive drainage work which has been carried out since World War II has considerably reduced the flooding, to the improvement of agriculture but not, I fear, to the benefit of wintering wildfowl or the fenland flora and fauna. Much of this land is less than 20ft above sea level and although encroachments of the sea have now been prevented, sea water reached Glastonbury, some fifteen miles inland, as recently as the end of World War II.

Aquatic plants which live in running water can be classified in various ways. One way is to separate them according to their ecological preferences and then subdivide them into three categories; those with submerged, those with floating and those with aerial vegetation. Even such a restricted and seemingly uncomplicated habitat as a river has a complex vegetational pattern.

In the clear fast-flowing stretches water crowfoot *Ranunculus pseudo-fluitans* is the characteristic and dominant plant. An allied species *R. fluitans* occurs in the same habitat but it is much more local except in the Thames, where it is abundant in some stretches, and in Dorset, where it appears more common than the former species. Accompanying water crowfoot are several of the pondweeds *Potamogeton* spp. The Loddon pondweed *P. nodosus* is a rare and very localised plant found only in the Loddon, the Thames, the Bristol Avon and the Stour. An extremely rare hybrid pondweed *P. acutifolius* × *berchtoldii* is in Britain found only at Arne in Dorset. Fool's watercress *Apium nodiflorum* is sometimes the dominant plant of these fast-running stretches. The common watercress *Rorippa nasturtium-aquaticum* is often abundant.

The slower meandering stretches of a chalk stream have more plants. Under the water grows in profusion the Canadian pondweed *Elodea canadensis*. This North American aquatic was introduced into this country in 1836 and spread so rapidly that it soon became a very common plant in British rivers. It is, however, subject to fluctuations, reaching a peak of abundance and then declining when the environment can no longer sustain its density.

On the water surface is another small and common plant, the water starwort *Callitriche* spp. Of the emergent vegetation, water parsnip *Sium latifolium*, river water dropwort *Oenanthe fistulosa*, mare's tail *Hippuris vulgaris*, figwort *Scrophularia* spp and water speedwell *Veronica anagallis-aquatica* are typical species, but there is a very varied distributional pattern and what is frequent in one district may be scarce in others. The veronica just mentioned occasionally hybridises with the pink water speedwell *V. catenata*. In 1967 the river Meon at Meonstoke was invaded by this vigorous tall-growing hybrid which spreads by vegetative reproduction.

When the stream leaves the chalk the water still remains calcareous but the bottom gradually becomes more silted and additional species enter the plant community. These include the mainly submerged spiked milfoil *Myriophyllum spicatum*, the yellow water lily *Nuphar lutea* on the surface, and in shallow water near the bank the flag iris *Iris pseudocorus*, flote-grass *Glyceria fluitans* and giant flote-grass *G. maxima*.

The animal life of a river is almost always near at hand and yet so tantalisingly hidden in the water weeds below the surface. Fortunately, freshwater animals can be easily collected and kept in a glass tank with the important proviso that the more rapacious predators are rigidly excluded. Much of the animal life is minute, belonging to little-studied groups, and there is space here to mention only a few of the larger kinds inhabiting the slower reaches. The freshwater shrimp *Gammarus pulex* is extremely common in the chalk streams. The crayfish *Astacus fluviatilis* is another and much larger member of the Crustacea and not a fish at all. It lurks under banks and is not easily seen but is probably more common than realised. It certainly occurs in a number of rivers within the region and is abundant in some places, such as in the Avon north of Salisbury. A worm new to Britain was discovered in May 1964 in a crayfish at Reading and even more surprisingly in 1954 a Bath canal produced an Asiatic worm.

The nymphs of a few species of dragonfly are found in these rivers; the commonest is the demoiselle agrion *Agrion virgo* and another damsel fly of this habitat is the white-legged *Platycnemis pennipes*. The banded agrion *A. splendens* is more a creature of quiet streams and not so typical of large rivers, but it is nevertheless abundant on the Kennet and Thames. Of the larger hawker dragonflies, two kinds occur in running water, the club-tail *Gomphus vulgatissima* which is found in Hampshire, Dorset and along the Thames at Reading, and the golden-ringed *Cordulegaster boltonii* found in Hampshire, Dorset and Somerset. In early summer the hatch of the mayflies is one of the great annual events in the life of a chalk stream as the trout leap greedily out of the water, following their depredations on the larvae with aerial assaults on the adult insects. The Kennet in Berkshire is noted for its tremendous mayfly hatches and several rare species are found along this river and the Thames.

Like dragonflies, most water bugs live in stagnant waters but a few inhabit rivers. One which lives entirely under water in fairly fast-flowing calcareous streams throughout most of the region is *Aphelocheirus aestivalus*. Two bugs of the surface film of large streams are the river pondskater *Aquarius najas* and the water cricket *Velia caprai*. Water beetles, too, are more common in still waters but a few species live in the slower reaches and along the stream margins. Several uncommon species have a very specialised habitat in moss growing in waterfalls and are found on the Mendips. The most striking of these is the small blue staphylid *Dianous coerulescens*.

The Hampshire chalk streams, particularly the Test, are famous for their trout and salmon fisheries. It is not only naturalists but also the general public who enjoy watching the salmon leap the weirs in late autumn on their way to the spawning shallows. Two good spots to see this spectacle are on the Itchen Navigation at Bishopstoke and on the Test at Romsey.

Where the Avon is concerned, coarse fishing is more important and as a consequence there is a good variety of fish. There are the bottom feeders such as brook lamprey, stone loach, bullhead, gudgeon and barbel. The last two are decidedly scarce but the barbel, which is of great interest to anglers for its fighting abilities, seems to be slowly spreading up river in recent years. Then there are minnows, chub, dace, roach, grayling and pike. The presence of a sluggish water species like roach and a swift river species like dace indicates that the Avon has alternating stretches. Old pike sometimes reach a gigantic size: one caught on the Avon at Fordingbridge in 1944 weighed 47lb.

The Thames stands in a class of its own as Britain's premier river. The commonest fish is the bleak, of which it is estimated that there are some two and a half million in the Reading section alone. Roach is the second commonest fish, and among the rest are perch with its small and scarce relative, pope, and also bream and gudgeon. There are considerable variations in the fish populations of neighbouring rivers: it is, for example, surprising that while bleak is so abundant in the Thames it is absent from

Page 71 (*above*) Coniferous woodland at Ramscombe in the Quantocks; (*below*) larva of buff-tip moth, a common defoliant on oak

Page 72 (*above*) Old Winchester Hill national nature reserve—pheasant covert left foreground, frog orchid slope with yew and hawthorn scrub in centre, small exhibition hut right distance; (*below*) ground thistle, a common plant of chalk downs

nearby rivers, and conversely that whereas only a few trout are found in the Thames they are abundant in its tributary the Pang.

The west-flowing Somerset rivers have good numbers of coarse fish and to those already mentioned can be added tench, carp and rudd, three species which indicate the sluggish nature of these rivers.

Only a few British mammals are adapted to life in water. Water voles are common and widely distributed in central southern England. They are attractive creatures, harmless except for the occasional damage they do to banks, and it is a great pity that they are known to country people as water rats for they are not even in the same family, let alone genus. Some years ago the bones of water vole were found during archaeological investigations at a Bronze Age barrow on Salisbury Plain. This was a rather puzzling discovery, indicating possibly that water voles were then more terrestial in habit, but there could be, of course, other explanations. Although water shrews are the largest of their kind they are only half the size of the water vole. Reports of their presence are infrequent and it is clear they are a local species and perhaps to be found more frequently in small streams and ditches, as for example in the Pang valley in Berkshire and the Avon valley near Salisbury. They do, however, also live in the main river Avon.

Otters have declined greatly in recent years and are now scarce although widely distributed. They are fairly common in south Dorset where the river Frome is a favourite haunt, on the upper reaches of the Thames and in the fen country around Langport in Somerset. They are nocturnal creatures and due to persecution have become very secretive, so that one hopes with faint optimism that the situation is not quite so bad as it appears. If they were given protection there would seem to be no reason why they should not increase again. Due to their wandering habits otters occasionally become road casualties, as in Weymouth in 1969 when two were found dead on the road. Often this is the only way their presence in a district becomes known, although along river courses their distinctive tracks and spraint deposited at regular dropping places reveal their whereabouts to the observant eye. The otter may travel long distances over land, and in 1967 one was found shot on a Berkshire down several miles from the nearest water.

The mink is a new addition to the British mammalian fauna. From about 1955 onwards escapes began from mink farms. Like the grey squirrel in woodland the mink soon obtained for himself an ecological niche and spread rapidly. There are now well-established breeding colonies on most of the rivers in the region. It is a ferocious predator and has attacked salmon in the lower reaches of the Avon, but despite urgent control measures has continued to spread.

The bat of the waterside is Daubenton's, common and widespread in southern England. It is slightly larger than the pipistrelle with which it is often confused, and it can often be seen on summer evenings flying low along the river, hawking insects.

Along slow-moving rivers the moorhen, mallard and swan are almost certain to be present. The only diving birds are the coot and little grebe, locally common on quiet stretches. Both in 1966 and 1967 at Britford near Salisbury little grebes were found choked to death while attempting to swallow bullheads. Pied and grey wagtails are usually closely associated with water although they do not necessarily breed along streamsides. Kingfishers, severely hit by the hard winter of 1963 and now recovering, are widely distributed but local, and often move to the coast in winter. Dippers are uncommon breeding birds within the region, nesting in scattered localities in Wiltshire, Dorset and Somerset. It has been estimated that about sixteen pairs nest in Dorset, all in the western half of the county.

Canals

An extensive network of canals covers the region. They are largely disused so far as their original purpose of transporting goods is concerned, but dedicated enthusiasts have been active in promoting their restoration for amenity purposes and some may become multi-use waters serving the interests of fishing, boating and nature study. Their commercial disuse has brought silting and an abundance of plants with a consequent increase in wildlife. Noted canals include the Itchen Navigation from Southampton to Winchester, the Basingstoke Canal which ran from Basingstoke to Byfleet in Surrey, the Kennet and Avon which joins the Bristol Avon with the Thames at Reading, and the Bridgewater Canal linking Taunton, the county town of Somerset, with the coast at Bridgwater.

A description of what can be seen on the Basingstoke Canal will indicate the wealth of plant and animal life. Below the surface are dense masses of the aquatic willow moss *Fontinalis antipyretica* and the river water dropwort, sometimes so abundant that the plants seriously impede the flow of water. On the stems of the willow moss live many freshwater sponges. Other plants with wholly or mainly submerged leaves are the water milfoil, water crowfoot *Ranunculus peltatus*, the uncommon water violet *Hottonia palustris* and that strange plant the water soldier *Stratiotes aloides* which rises to the surface for flowering and then slowly subsides below the surface again.

On the surface of the canal there are three species of pondweed, frogbit *Hydrocharis morsus-ranae*, yellow and white water lilies, the former being the commoner, three kinds of duckweed *Lemna* spp and masses of fool's watercress. The algal blanket-weed *Spirogyra* sp carpets the water and surface vegetation. The water fern *Azolla filiculoides* was once common but now seems to have declined, for the time being at any rate. This is an American plant which first appeared in Britain in 1883 and which can spread rapidly in optimum conditions. In the autumn the leaves turn red. There is a delightful story of evacuees from London arriving in north Wiltshire at the beginning of World War II and finding the Kennet and Avon canal so smothered with *Azolla* that it looked like a road of red granite. This, they were convinced, was an invention of the government to mislead German aircraft!

The emergent vegetation includes the following:

sedges	*Carex* spp
common reed	*Phragmites communis*
reed grass	*Phalaris arundinacea*
bur reed	*Sparganium erectum*
reed mace	*Typha latifolia*
flag iris	*Iris pseudocorus*

Invertebrate aquatic life is present in abundance. Among fish there are pike, perch and tench, among amphibians frogs and toads, and among reptiles grass snakes which are as at home in water as on the land. This is an ideal habitat for water voles and here I have enjoyed watching them nibbling at the base of reed stems like miniature beavers. On hot summer days dragonflies shimmer over the water; they include both *Agrions*, the downy emerald *Cordulia aenea* and the fine emperor *Anax imperator*.

The often dense vegetation on the banks means that in addition to the birds of the waterside such as moorhen, reed bunting, sedge warbler and kingfisher there can be seen tits, nightingales, blackcaps, garden warblers and many others.

Still waters

There is a surprising variety of types in the still waters of the region. There are first of all the large ornamental lakes constructed for the great country estates of the eighteenth and nineteenth centuries. Typical examples of such waters are Avington Lake in Hampshire, Virginia Water in Berkshire, Longleat in Wiltshire, Sherborne Lake in Dorset and Cricket St Thomas in Somerset. Larger still are the reservoirs built principally for water supplies although a few were constructed to supply canals. A number of these in Somerset are of great ornithological importance, as are the flooded mineral workings such as the clay pits around Bridgwater and the gravel pits along the Thames valley.

Then there are natural ponds, mill ponds, dew ponds, village ponds, temporary pools, ditches, flooded meadows and the sewage farms with their lagoons, so unsalubrious to humans, so enticing to waders, and now passing out of existence as modern sewage works are constructed. The Blue Pool near Wareham comes in a category of its own and is a tourist attraction. The unusual colour is caused by diffraction of light from suspended particles of clay.

Pondweeds, sedges, rushes, reed mace, duckweed, starwort and milfoil are common plants of stagnant water but in a few places uncommon plants occur. The small and unprepossessing *Ludwigia palustris* was first discovered in Britain about 1660 in shallow water near Heath Pond at Petersfield in Hampshire. It has long since disappeared from there but until recently grew in a pond in a Southampton suburb and still grows in the New Forest. Shoreweed *Littorella uniflora* is a very local plant which occurs in a few places in south Dorset, north Wiltshire and on the Mendips. It has been recorded as growing plentifully at Durleigh Reservoir, near Bridgwater.

The smaller waters with much vegetation are the richest in invertebrate life but there is plenty of scope for distributional and ecological studies of pond life throughout the region, as the composition of the fauna varies from pond to pond. Creatures common to virtually all of them are worms of many kinds, water fleas (which are not fleas at all but minute crustaceans) whose numbers fluctuate throughout the summer, beetles, water bugs, dragonfly and caddis larvae.

The great silver water-beetle *Hydrophilus piceus* is a fine creature and must be one of Britain's largest beetles but unfortunately it is not common; the great diving beetle *Dytiscus marginalis* by contrast is frequently found, as are species in the genera *Agabus*, *Haliplus* and *Hydroporus*. The screech beetle *Hygrobia tarda*, which has the unusual habit of emitting a sound by rubbing the elytra on the abdomen, is of local occurrence. On the surface clusters of whirligig beetles *Gyrinus* spp are frequent. Some rare beetles are found within the region. *Haliplus furcatus* was first recorded in Britain during World War I in a Somerset pond and is known only from one or two ponds in that county. *Graphoderus cinereus* is a rare beetle recorded only from eastern England until some specimens were discovered in north Hampshire in 1952. There are two weevils which have become adapted to an aquatic existence and one of them, *Eubrychius velatus*, is a very local species which has been recorded from the Bridgwater area of Somerset.

Many kinds of water bug live in the lakes and ponds. There are pond skaters *Gerris* spp skimming the surface, water scorpions *Nepa cinerea*, saucer bugs *Ilyocoris cimicoides*, pondweed bugs *Mesovelia furcata*, sphagnum bugs *Hebrus* spp, water boatmen *Notonecta* spp and Corixids which are sometimes known as lesser boatmen. Although all these are found in stagnant water they do not all occur together; there are various micro-habitats and many species have a definite preference for one type. The fauna of a pond is not static but as the vegetation proliferates or changes its character so too does the species composition of the fauna change. Some, such as pondweed and sphagnum bugs, are found on aquatic vegetation; some, like water measurers and pond skaters, live on the quiet margins; clear water with a sandy bottom is required by the water singer *Micronecta poweri*, whilst the saucer bug and water scorpion demand muddy pools; calcareous water is the preference of some Corixid species, acid peaty pools are the habitat of the water boatman *Notonecta glauca*, and deep pools are favoured by the water stick-insect *Ranatra linearis*. The amount of organic material present is another significant factor affecting distribution. *Micronecta minutissima* is an erratic migrant which may suddenly appear in a new locality and may build up an immense population for a short time. This happened at Longleat in Wiltshire during 1943 where a large temporary population occurred. *Glaenocorisa propinqua* is an interesting water bug in that it is probably a glacial relict species; it exists in Britain from the Midlands northwards, though it still survives in one pond in north Somerset.

The nymphs of most dragonflies live in stagnant water and

the region is rich in species, some of them rare. Of the 44 British species 35 occur in Hampshire, and Dorset is not far behind with 29. In the damsel flies the large red *Pyrrhosoma nymphula*, the common ischnura *Ischnura elegans*, the common blue *Enallagma cyathigerum* and the common coenagrion *Coenagrion puella* are widespread. Widely distributed, but more local, are the small red *Ceriagrion tenellum*, the red-eyed *Erythromma najas*, the variable coenagrion *C. pulchellum* and the green lestes *Lestes sponsa.*

In the darter group the common sympetrum *S. striolatum*, the black-lined orthetrum *O. cancellatum*, the four-spotted libellula *L. quadrimaculata*, and others are fairly common generally. Although the downy emerald *Cordulia aenea* is widely distributed, in Somerset it is known only from two localities, one of which is Priddy Pools high on the Mendips. These pools, a photograph of which appears on page 17, formed on the site of old lead-workings, and with masses of water horsetail *Equisetum fluviatile* and bottle sedge *Carex rostrata*, are of considerable interest. No fewer than fourteen species of dragonfly breed in them. Rare darter dragonflies are the brilliant emerald *Somatochloras metallica* which in the region is known only from a few Hampshire localities, the orange-spotted emerald *Oxygastra curtisii* probably from only one spot in Hampshire, and the scarce libellula *Libellula fulva* from only one locality in Dorset.

The commonest of the large hawker dragonflies is the southern aeshna *A. cyanea* although its status in Berkshire is doubtful. The hairy dragonfly *Brachytron pratense*, common aeshna *A. juncea*, brown aeshna *A. grandis* and the emperor *Anax imperator* are more local. The brown aeshna, surprisingly, is common in north Hampshire but scarce in the south of the county.

There are a few spiders associated with ponds. The raft spider *Dolomedes fimbriatus* is a magnificent creature found locally on the surface of peaty pools. The water spider *Argyroneta aquatica* lives below the surface in a specially constructed bell of air designed long before man thought of the bathysphere. Other spiders are typically found in the reeds bordering the pond and include such species as *Clubiona phragmites*, *Araneus cornutus* and *Tetragnatha extensa*.

The three species of newts, smooth, palmate and crested, are widely distributed, the last being the scarcest and most local. In many places the first two species are equally common but the smooth newt appears to be the species of the Thames valley. Frogs seem to have declined in the region in line with the national trend but toads have been recorded as fairly common in recent years, even with slight increases in some places.

The fish which are most at home in still waters are carp, roach, tench, pike and eels. Fish living in the optimum conditions of a lake often grow to a large size: one carp removed from Hiltingbury Lake in Hampshire during cleaning operations in 1971 weighed 23lb, which is close to the record for English waters. Occasionally, still waters suffer from de-oxygenation in summer for various reasons, prolonged drought and excess sewage effluent among them. When this happens fish mortality takes place on a large scale, as happened in July 1956 at a small mill pond in the Hampshire village of Bishops Waltham when several thousand roach were seen floating on the surface, their silvery-white bodies dotting the pond like giant snowflakes.

Coots, moorhens, little grebes, mallard and swans are the common birds of lakes and ponds. The water rail too is widespread but much more local. The numbers of great crested grebe have increased in recent years and breed regularly on the larger waters, particularly on flooded gravel pits and reservoirs. This is one of the few cases where building development has been indirectly beneficial: the increase in worked-out gravel pits has provided additional habitats for the species.

The disused gravel pit in its early stages often provides a suitable habitat for the nesting of little ringed plovers, that is, when shallow pools left by winter flooding are surrounded with bare gravel or gravel as yet colonised only by dwarf annual plants. Once the vegetation has grown dense the site loses its attractions. This bird is still a rare breeding species in the region, nesting erratically in very small numbers in the eastern part. Berkshire is a relative stronghold with nests in most years since 1947 and a maximum of fifteen pairs recorded. The first record for Hampshire was in 1952 and in 1970 a pair nested in Wiltshire.

Apart from mallard few other ducks nest; small numbers of teal breed in scattered localities and garganey occasionally in Somerset; a few pochard are irregular nesters; gadwall have commenced nesting in recent years at Chew Valley Reservoir; tufted duck have nested sporadically in Hampshire since World War II and breed in small numbers in Wiltshire and Berkshire, but the principal breeding haunt of this duck is at Chew, where well over a hundred pairs nest each year; this locality is also virtually the only breeding area in the region for shoveler and for the ruddy duck, an alien species which has established itself in the wild. Another introduced species is the mandarin duck, some twenty pairs of which breed at Virginia Water and other pairs live in a semi-feral state at Leckford on the river Test in Hampshire.

The picture in winter is very different, with accumulations of waterfowl on the larger inland waters. There are many lakes which are worth visiting in winter but Chew is surely pre-eminent for both the quantity and quality of its birds. The reservoir here was only completed in 1956 by the flooding of the upper reaches of the river Chew, but the submerged meadows provided optimum conditions for the fish, which have flourished, and the birds have benefited by the amount of aquatic food available, the extent of open water and the wooded surroundings. There are small numbers of great crested grebe, cormorants, Bewick swans, golden-eye and pintail usually seen with much larger numbers of mallard, teal, wigeon, shoveler, pochard, tufted duck and coot. The water pipit is a scarce passage migrant here in spring. Chew has gained a well-deserved reputation as a place where anything may turn up—the white-winged black tern, the spoonbill or the gyr falcon—but perhaps its greatest sensation was the presence there of an American bird, the pied-billed grebe, for long periods in 1965–6. Chew is a superb bird-watching area, but the merits of other waters ought

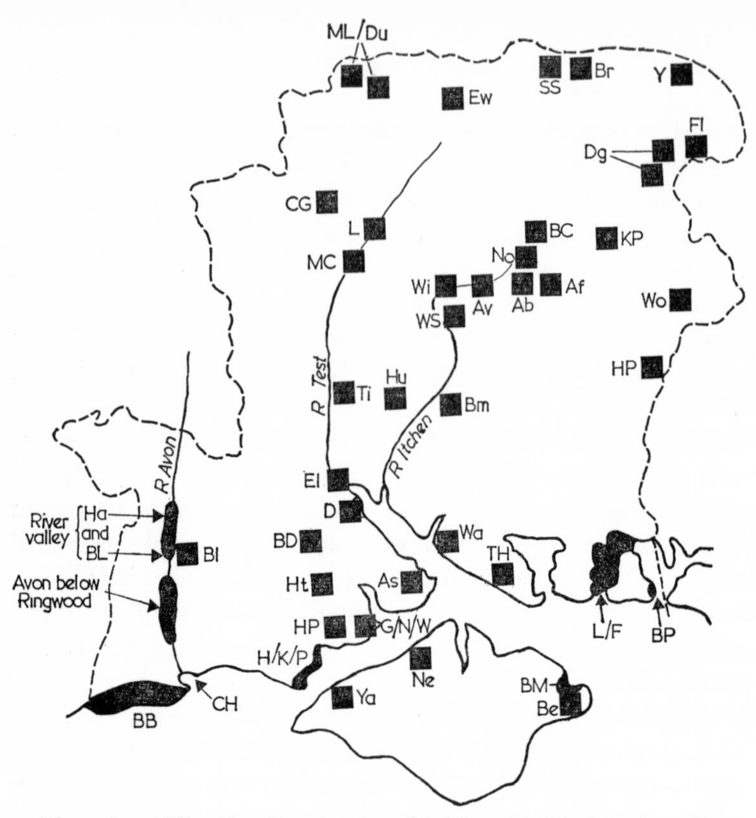

The main wildfowl localities in Hampshire from *Wildfowl in Hampshire* by J. H. Taverner

Ab	Alrebury	H/K/P	Hurst/Keyhaven/Pennington
Af	Alresford	HP	Heath Pond
As	Ashlett Creek	Ht	Hatchet Pond
Av	Avington	Hu	Hursley Park Pond
BB	Bournemouth Bay	KP	Kings Pond
BC	Brown Candover	L	Leckford
BD	Bishop's Dyke	L/F	Langstone/Farlington Marsh
Be	Bembridge	MC	Marsh Court
Bl	Blashford Gravel Pits	ML/Du	Milford Lake/Dunsmere
BM	Brading Marsh	Ne	Newtown
Bm	Brambridge	No	Northington
BP	Black Point	SCP	St Catherine's Point
Br	Bramshill	SP	Sowley Pond
CG	Charlton Gravel Pits	SS	Stratfield Saye
CH	Christchurch Harbour	TH	Titchfield Haven
Dg	Dogmersfield Lakes	Ti	Timsbury
Di	Dibden Bay	Wa	Warsash
El	Eling Marsh	Wi	Winnall
Ew	Ewhurst	Wo	Woolmer
Fl	Fleet Pond	WS	Winchester Sewage Farm
G/N/W	Gins/Needs Oar/Warren	Y	Yateley gravel pit
Ha & BL	Harbridge and the river at Blashford	Ya	Yarmouth

not to be overlooked. The neighbouring reservoirs of Blagdon and Cheddar, for example, are also very good. In general, numbers of wildfowl are smaller in Wiltshire, Dorset and Berkshire, but Hampshire closely rivals, and in the case of one or two species is possibly better than, Somerset. It is strange that wigeon which is the commonest wintering duck in Hampshire and Somerset should be so disproportionately scarce in Wiltshire.

Even quite small ponds are not without interest. A small impermanent pond in western Hampshire has a remarkable inhabitant. It is a small crustacean, by name *Triops cancriformis*, and this is probably its only locality in England. Its habitat requirements are very specialised for it needs warm water in a pond which dries up after it has laid its eggs. This condition is of course not easily obtained and this no doubt accounts for its great rarity. Another example of an animal adapting itself to the conditions provided by temporary ponds is that of the freshwater snail *Sphaerium lacustre* which occurs commonly in field ponds and is able to maintain itself during the dry period.

The clay-lined dew ponds of the chalk downs are of artificial origin, being constructed to supply the needs of agriculture. Wiltshire once had many but they have fallen into disuse and some have become dry. Those that are left commonly have broad-leaved pondweed and water crowfoot on the surface with common spike-rush *Eleocharis palustris* round the margins. Insects which are especially typical of Wiltshire dewponds are the water boatmen *Notonecta obliqua* with the variety *delcourti* and a lesser water boatman *Sigura limitata.*

Marshlands and river margins

Rivers bring down vast quantities of alluvial silt which in the course of geological time overlay the existing soil in a broad band on each side of the river. Here, the water level being always near or above the surface, extensive marshlands were formed. Today, however, agricultural land drainage schemes have reduced these marshlands to a fraction of their former size.

As a consequence, many floristic and faunal changes are made. In 1948 an elementary ecological survey was made of an interesting 8 acre marsh bordering the river Itchen on the outskirts of Southampton. Not long afterwards, it became successively a local authority refuse tip and then a pleasure ground. It has been 'tidied up' and has a smooth grass sward, but the marsh plants have gone and the grasshopper warbler sings there no more.

Despite drainage projects there are still numerous small areas of marsh, and river borders often have a marsh flora. Typical plants include: purple loosestrife *Lythrum salicaria*, yellow loosestrife *Lysimachia vulgaris*, flote grass *Glyceria maxima*, common reed *Phragmites communis*, reed grass *Phalaris arundinacea*, bur reed *Sparganium* spp, yellow flag *Iris pseudocorus*, figwort *Scrophularia nodosa*, water mint *Mentha aquatica*, meadowsweet *Filipendula ulmaria*, marsh bedstraw *Galium palustre*, marsh marigold *Caltha palustris*, comfrey *Symphytum officinale*. Many others flourish in this habitat for the alluvial soil is rich in organic matter and nutrients. The sweet flag *Acorus calamus* is an introduced plant which is extremely scarce in the region; it appears to be most plentiful in Berkshire where it grows along the Thames and its tributaries. Swans are fond of it and may have helped in spreading it.

The small Berkshire village of Marcham shows an interesting variation from the usual vegetative pattern. A salt-water spring outcropping at the junction of the Corallian Limestone with Kimmeridge Clay has produced a salt-marsh flora of mud rush *Juncus gerardii*, sea spurrey *Spergularia marina*, sea club-rush *Scirpus maritimus* and celery *Apium graveolens*, altogether an astonishing sight some sixty miles from the coast.

Alder and willow carr mark the next step in the ecological succession from marsh and swamp. Associated shrubs may include alder-buckthorn *Frangula alnus*, guelder rose *Viburnum opulus*, blackcurrant *Ribes nigrum*, and privet *Ligustrum vulgare*. Several kinds of fern and moss occur here and the fungus *Polyporus radiatus* is sometimes found on the alder trunks. The large and local musk beetle *Aromia moschata* is associated with old willows and one of the localities where it occurs is along the banks of the river Itchen. Another local, smaller beetle found on sallow is *Lochmaea cuprea*. The larvae of the dingy shell moth *Euchoeca nebulata* feed on alder, as do those of the alder moth *Apatele alni* which however is not restricted to alder; it is a local species although it has been increasingly seen in recent years.

The meadow grasshopper *Chorthippus parallelus* and slender ground-hopper *Tetrix subulata* are fairly common but that extraordinary insect the mole cricket *Grylotalpa grylotalpa* is known in the region only from the water meadows at Christchurch and in the Test valley.

Among the beetles, the brilliant leaf beetles *Donacia vulgaris* and *O. marginata* are widespread on bur reed. A number of weevils are found on specific marsh plants. *Grypus equisetis* is widely distributed on field and marsh horsetail; the tiny *Nanophye gracilis*, which within the region is found in Hampshire and Berkshire on water purslane *Peplis portula*; *N. marmoratus* which is rather more generally distributed on purple loosestrife and *Gymnetron beccabungae* which is a local species on brooklime. The figwort beetles *Cionus* spp are widely if somelocally distributed. These are very good examples of protective coloration, the pupa bearing a marked resemblance to the seed capsules of the figwort on which it lives.

A number of plant bugs are associated with plants of the marshes. The broad damsel bug *Nabis flavomarginatus* and the marsh damsel bug *Dolichonabis limbatus* live in the coarse vegetation of the water meadows. A capsid bug *Polymerus palustris* feeds on marsh bedstraw; within the region it has been recorded from Hampshire and it may well occur in some at least of the other counties. As in other insect orders, there are some bugs which are of continental distribution but which nevertheless live in southern England either because they are on the edge of their range or because they are a thrusting species expanding their range. *Adelphocoris ticinensis*, a south European species found in the coastal counties of the region, is perhaps an example of the first kind. The European chinch bug *Ischnodemus sabuleti* illustrates the second type, for in the last forty years it has spread outwards from one locality in south-east England and in its westward movement has now reached the marshlands of Hampshire and Berkshire, feeding on reeds and grasses.

Moths of many different species fly in the marshes. Common and widespread species include the straw dot *Rivula sericealis*, the blood vein *Calothysamis amata*, the drinker *Philudoria potatoria* and several kinds of wainscots which inhabit the reedbeds. The following are examples of species which are more local although they may be common in some places: dingy footman *Eilema griseola*, round-winged muslin *Comacla senex*, oblique carpet *Orthonama lignata*, marsh oblique-barred *Hypenodes turfosalis*, pinion-streaked snout *Schrankia costaestrigalis*. An exotic moth is the scarlet tiger *Panaxia dominula*, a widespread but local species, not found in Somerset. The larvae feed on comfrey and on a riverside walk in June one may sometimes come across a mass emergence of the moths. Places where they can be seen include the Itchen valley in Hampshire and in Berkshire the valley of the Kennet. The scarce burnished brass *Plusia chryson* lives up to its name but occurs in the Itchen and Test valleys where the larvae feed on hemp agrimony.

Butterflies of this habitat are the green-veined white *Pieris napi*, the orange-tip *Euchloe cardamines*, the brimstone *Gonepteryx rhamni* and the marsh fritillary *Euphydryas aurinia*. The first three are common but the last is local although sometimes plentiful.

The small breeding passerines are reed bunting, sedge, reed and grasshopper warblers. Reed buntings are the only resident birds in that list. They are a common sight in the reed beds uttering their apology of a song, but recently there has been a tendency for them to appear in drier habitats and they have been known to turn up at a bird table in the middle of a town. Grasshopper warblers are also moving to drier ground, particularly to young conifer plantations. Marsh warblers are rare but probably nest regularly in very small numbers in the western part of the region. Bearded tits have begun nesting regularly in at least one locality and breeding has taken place elsewhere. Increasingly in recent years birds have come as winter visitors to a number of reed beds throughout the region. Bitterns are following a somewhat similar pattern with single birds wintering at various places and in at least one Somerset locality remaining during the summer. Rare birds are occasionally seen in the reed beds, birds such as spotted crake and Cetti's warbler, the latter in *Phragmites* at Titchfield Haven in Hampshire in the spring of 1961 and at Thatcham, Berkshire, in the autumn of 1971. Water rails are characteristic birds of this habitat but are more often heard than seen and seem to be scarce in the breeding season. Birds of other habitats visit reed beds in winter, blue tits to feed and starlings in great numbers to roost. Siskins and lesser redpolls visit the alders.

In some of the watercress beds green sandpipers are increasingly over-wintering and, rarely, a water pipit may be present. A local summer migrant which nests in the water meadows is the yellow wagtail; it is scarce in Hampshire and Dorset but fairly common in north Wiltshire and Somerset. The water meadows of the Hampshire Avon are regularly visited each winter by a flock of white-fronted geese more than a thousand strong.

Fens

Whilst both marsh and fen are alkaline the former consists of silt and the latter of peat. Fenland exists in certain parts of the central southern region, in Berkshire, for instance, notably in the small village of Cothill where hollows in the Corallian Limestone contain peat deposits.

This is an interesting and important area of fen at Cothill, most of it comprised in two reserves, the Nature Conservancy Ruskin reserve and another leased by the county naturalists' trust. It is, in a way, an unexpected habitat to find in this limestone district, for the approach along a tree-lined path from the village gives little indication of the large expanse of fen lying just ahead. Here, apart from bog plants such as butterwort

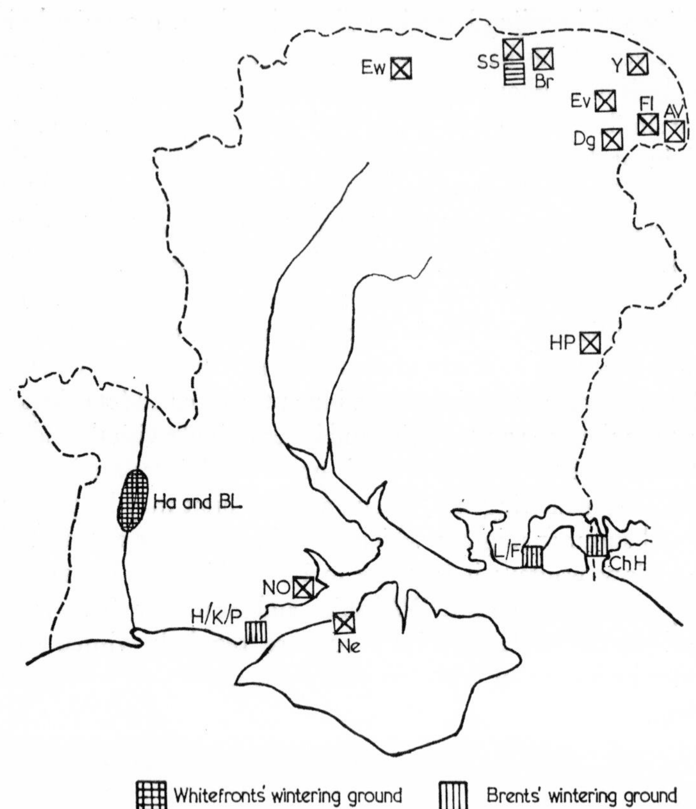

The distribution of geese in Hampshire from *Wildfowl in Hampshire* by J. H. Taverner

AV	Ash Vale
Br	Bramshill
Ch H	Chichester Harbour
Ev	Elvetham Lake
Ew	Ewhurst
Dg	Dogmersfield Lakes
Fl	Fleet Pond
Ha & BL	Harbridge and the river at Blashford
H/K/P	Hurst/Keyhaven/Pennington
HP	Heath Pond
L/F	Langstone/Farlington Marsh
Ne	Newtown
NO	Needs Oar
SS	Stratfield Saye
Y	Yateley gravel pit

Page 89 (*above*) A Hampshire beech wood with large white helleborine in centre foreground; (*below*) badger gate in Castle Neroche forest, Somerset

Page 90 (*above*) Song thrush feeding young, a common bird of garden, woods and farmland hedgerows; (*below left*) white admiral, a fine butterfly of oak woodland; (*below right*) spiked star of Bethlehem, a rare plant but locally abundant in some Somerset ashwoods

Pinguicula vulgaris, bog bean *Menyanthes trifoliata* and bog pimpernel *Anagallis tenella*, there are many marsh flowers and sedges including the early marsh orchid *Dactylorchis incarnata*, the fen orchid *D. praetermissa*, the narrow-leaved marsh orchid *D. traunsteineria*, the fragrant orchid *Gymnadenia conopsea* var *densiflora*, and others. The vegetation is dense so that walking is tough going and care is needed in the deeper parts. The larvae of the marsh fritillary feeds on devil's bit *Succisa pratensis* and the Cothill colony of scarlet tiger moths has been the subject of intensive genetic studies by Professor E. B. Ford.

But by far the largest areas of fen are in Somerset in the North Levels between the Liassic outcrops of the Poldens and Wedmore ridge, and they consist of a number of moors. Similar moors form the South Levels east of Taunton and are divided into two by the Curry ridge, south-west of Langport, although these southern moors consist mainly of alluvium. In the north-west of the county, too, there is another area of peat in the Gordano valley. These are fascinating districts, resembling to some extent the East Anglian fens, but they are now mere fragments of their former extent. They once encircled Glastonbury Tor and similar isolated Liassic outcrops which rose like islands from what in prehistoric times must have been a virtual swamp. In the neighbourhood of Glastonbury remains of lake villages have been discovered. The many bird bones found reveal the rich avian fauna of 2,400 years ago, including such species as Dalmatian pelican, white-tailed eagle, red kite and crane. The white-tailed eagle was already in Somerset 400,000 years earlier as the bone fauna of Clevedon Cave reveals.

Tremendous changes in the Somerset fens have taken place in this century. Extensive flooding used to be a matter of course every winter and many people have horrifying stories to tell of drownings and narrow escapes when carts missed the road and plunged into the side ditches. The installation of pumping stations has ensured that this type of flooding is a thing of the past but land drainage inevitably means considerable changes in the vegetation pattern.

There is a complex ecological history of these fenlands. Briefly, after the Pleistocene period there was a marine invasion of west Somerset which resulted in the deposition of layers of blue clay. By about 3500 BC the sea had receded and a brackish reed swamp had begun the process of peat formation. Differing conditions resulted in great fen sedge *Cladium mariscus* becoming abundant, followed by a woodland carr of birch, alder and willow. Next came cotton grass *Eriophorum* spp, deer grass *Trichophorum caespitosum* and *Sphagnum* and by this time the level was higher, producing a raised peat deposit. The peat depth varies and can be as much as 18ft. It is extracted principally for horticultural purposes but small quantities of peat blocks are dug out for fuel. The ecological succession at the present time proceeds from *Sphagnum* through *Eriophorum*, *Carex*, *Phragmites* to *Salix*, *Alnus* and *Betula pubescens* woodland.

The whole area has a rich bog and fen flora with local variations. The drainage ditches are known as rhynes and have a number of interesting aquatics. Of floating plants there are all

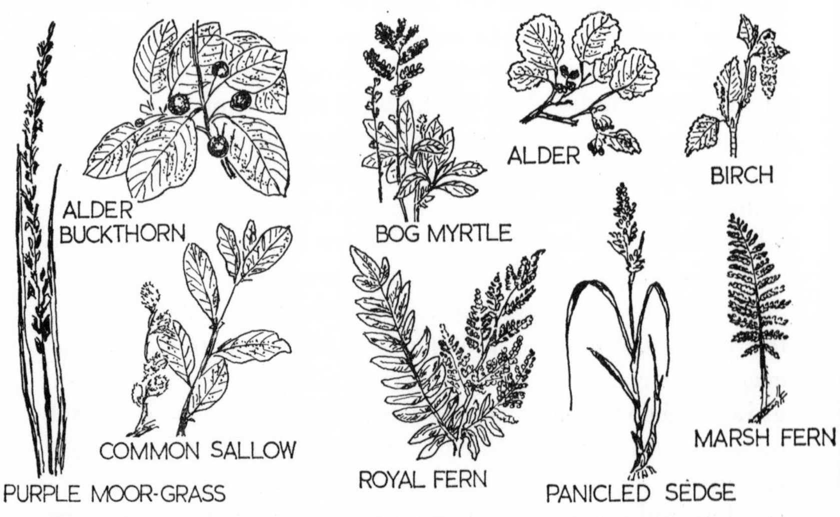

Plants occupying Somerset peat bogs before extraction of peat, from *Peat in Central Somerset* by Somerset County Council Planning Department

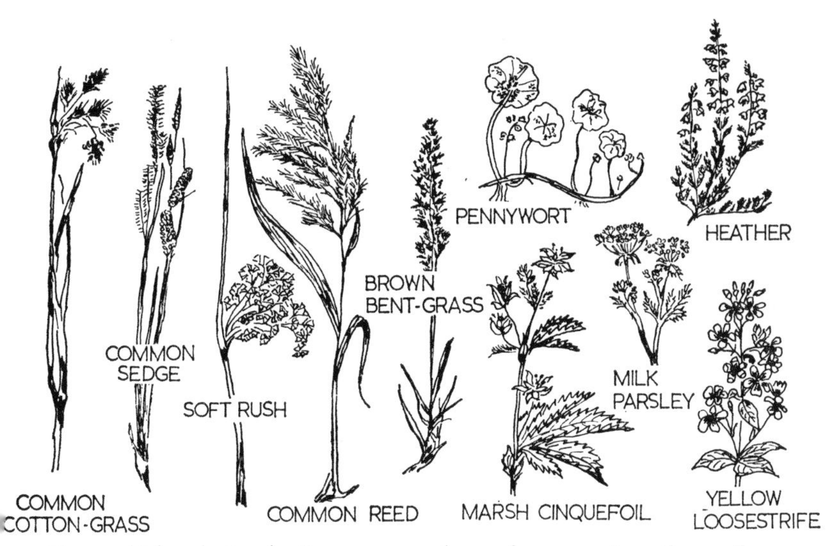

Plants which colonise the Somerset peat bogs after extraction of peat, from *Peat in Central Somerset* by Somerset County Council Planning Department

five species of duckweed, the water fern, frogbit, the partially submerged bladderworts *Utricularia* spp and the water violet *Hottonia palustris*. Emergent plants include arrowhead *Sagittaria sagittifolia*, water plantain *Alisma plantago-aquatica*, bur reed, greater water parsnip *Sium latifolium*, flote-grass and the common reed.

Among the dominant plants of the moors are the following: purple moor grass *Molinia caerulea*, brown bent *Agrostis canina*, water horsetail *Equisetum fluviatile*, yellow loosestrife *Lysimachia vulgaris*, marsh cinquefoil *Potentilla palustris*, panicled sedge *Carex paniculata*. The soft rush *Juncus effusus* and sedge *Carex nigra* are common in swampy areas and the marsh fern *Thelypteris palustris* is occasional here.

The royal fern *Osmunda regalis* (once described to me by a local inhabitant as 'Odd Mondays') is an uncommon plant of the carrs. Other specialities of the area include marsh pea *Lathyrus palustris*, milk parsley *Peucedanum palustre* and slender sedge *Carex lasiocarpa*, all locally plentiful although uncommon generally in England. The typical sedge of the fens, *Cladium mariscus*, was abundant in the past as indicated by plant remains and pollen in the peat but is now very rare. Other plants which have become less common are white beak sedge *Rhynchospora alba*, marsh andromeda *Andromeda polifolia* and cranberry *Vaccinium oxycoccus*. These are characteristic bog plants and show that there is no rigid clear-cut division between plants of bog, marsh and fen. The pH values range from acid to neutral and are able to support all three vegetational types. The last two, which are northern species, may even by now have become extinct. Further north in the Gordano valley the two rare marsh plants *Cyperus fuscus* and *C. longus* have been recorded.

These Somerset moors teem with a very rich insect life and only a small part of it can be referred to here. The great marsh grasshopper *Stethophyma grossus* is found and dragonflies are numerous. Butterflies include marsh fritillary and marbled whites. There is a great variety of moths and the following is a selective list of species which have been recorded on the fenland:

Moth		*Food plant*
emperor	*Saturnia pavonia*	various
pebble hook-tip	*Drepana falcataria*	birch and alder
cream-bordered green pea	*Earias clorana*	osiers
water ermine	*Spilosoma urticae* (decreasing)	various
scarlet tiger	*Panaxia dominula*	comfrey
miller	*Apatele leporina*	birch and alder
suspected	*Parastichtis suspecta*	birch and willow
double kidney	*Zenobia retusa*	birch and willow
silver hook	*Eustrotia uncula*	sedges
black neck	*Lygephilum pastinum*	tufted vetch
small seraphim	*Mysticoptera sexalisata*	sallow
shaded pug	*Eupithecia subumbrata*	compositae
slender pug	*E. tenuinata*	sallow
peacock	*Semiothisa notata*	birch and sallow
scallop shell	*Calocalpe undulata*	sallow
small scallop	*Sterrha emarginata*	bedstraw

The coleopterous fauna of the fens is exceptionally rich. Many beetles are associated with specific plants. In the rhynes, a tiny beetle *Tanysphyrus lemnae* is common, as its name implies, on duckweed, another weevil *Galerucella grisescens* feeds on yellow loosestrife, and there are numbers of water beetles. On the reed-mace in the swamps lives a tiny Clavicorn beetle *Telmatophilus typhae*. The weevil *Cryptorrhynchidius lapathi* can sometimes cause trouble on osier crops but it appears to be very local in Somerset.

Regular breeding birds of the moors are curlew, redshank, lapwing, snipe in small numbers, nightjars, lesser whitethroat, whinchat and grasshopper, reed and sedge warblers. In the South Levels, the scarce marsh warbler and probably also the corncrake occasionally nest. An ornithological event was the breeding of a pair of black-tailed godwit on the South Levels in 1963. On the cultivated parts, skylark and yellow wagtail can be seen. Willow tit, redstart and tree sparrow nest in the woodland. During the spring passage flocks of whimbrel are seen. Winter visitors include snipe, jack snipe in very small numbers, water rail, an occasional short-eared owl and hen harrier and numbers of duck and Bewick swans on the now limited areas of floodland near Langport and Draycott.

CHAPTER FOUR

Hills and downland

Chalk and Jurassic Limestone hills–Chalk scrub–The Mendips–The Quantocks

Chalk and Jurassic Limestone hills

A large proportion of the land surface of the region consists of calcareous soils. Much of it, of course, is farmland but in this chapter we are thinking only of the hilltops and the uncultivated hollows and combes. These, too, have been greatly modified by man. The vast sheep-walks of the eighteenth and nineteenth centuries have, in fact, manufactured the downland of the southern counties, the close-cropped turf developing a rich and distinctive flora. But times have changed and the downs have been subjected to a two-pronged attack from farmers and foresters.

Since World War II the emphasis on arable farming and the need for efficient economic units have brought more and more marginal land under the plough. Each year the tractor has gone higher up the hillside, destroying the downland habitat. Some areas remain untouched—patches that were too steep for cultivation or plots left alone because of the idiosyncrasies of individual farmers—but in general the downland, that was once so characteristic of southern England, is disappearing at an alarming rate. A matter of particular concern is the loss of the original grassland species.

The Nature Conservancy took action and in 1954 made the 140 acres of Old Winchester Hill in Hampshire a National Nature Reserve, following this in 1956 with 612 acres of Fyfield Down in Wiltshire. County naturalists' trusts have established a few more reserves, among them Oxenbourne and Catherington Downs in Hampshire, Hod Hill and Green Hill Down in Dorset, Aston Upthorpe and West Woodhay in Berkshire. County councils have also helped by the creation of public open spaces such as those at Danebury and Butser Hills in Hampshire. A representative and fairly well-spread selection of downland has thus been preserved, one hopes for ever, although frequent maintenance is required in the form of sheep grazing and removal of scrub.

Typical grasses of these calcareous hills are sheep and creeping fescue *Festuca ovina* and *F. rubra* in the short turf, with upright brome *Zerna erecta* and chalk false-brome *Brachypodium pinnatum* in coarse neglected grassland. An annual, the hard poa *Catapodium rigidum*, is common in places, especially on dry banks.

Various species of moss grow in chalk grassland and on limestone rocks. They often luxuriate on north slopes of the downs as at Old Winchester Hill where they have been gathered for commercial purposes. Common or locally plentiful species are *Ctenidium molluscum*, *Camptothecium lutescens* and *Neckera crispa.* Lichens are generally very scarce but the sarsen stones of the Berkshire downs carry a good variety, and a coastal lichen *Ramalina siliquosa* has been recorded inland on Salisbury Plain at Stonehenge and Avebury.

On the dry shallow soils of the chalk the flowering plants are often dwarfed. Prostrate forms are well adapted to these dry conditions and are frequent. They include the hoary plantain *Plantago media*, stemless thistle *Cirsium acaulon*, squinancywort *Asperula cynanchica*, and thyme *Thymus drucei.* Other dwarf flowers are the chalk milkwort *Polygala calcarea*, dwarf sedge *Carex humilis*, which is abundant on Salisbury Plain, and the purging flax *Linum catharticum.*

Typical of the rather larger plants are: salad burnet *Poterium sanguisorba*, kidney vetch *Anthyllis vulneraria*, horseshoe vetch *Hippocrepis comosa*, restharrow *Ononis repens*, dropwort *Filipendula vulgaris*, greater knapweed *Centaurea scabiosa*, clustered bellflower *Campanula glomerata*, harebell *Campanula rotundifolia.*

In the thistles the musk *Carduus nutans* and the woolly-headed *Cirsium eriophorum* are especially characteristic of calcareous grassland although neither is abundant. The rock rose *Helianthemum chamaecistus*, a dwarf shrub, is found on the chalk banks.

But to a botanist the merest mention of chalk downland is enough to make him dream of orchids. Unfortunately, in many species there has been a decline in numbers in recent years, a few have become extremely rare and one or two have apparently become extinct within the region. The only hopeful aspect is that orchids will sometimes reappear a number of years after their disappearance. The following is a list of the typical orchid species of calcareous grassland and their status in the region, most of them being more plentiful on the chalk than on the Jurassic strata: autumn lady's tresses *Spiranthes spiralis*, widely distributed but not plentiful; musk orchid *Herminium monorchis*, widespread but very uncommon; frog orchid *Coeloglossum viride*, local but widespread; fragrant orchid *Gymnadenia conopsea*, occasional; lesser butterfly orchid *Platanthera bifolia*, local, not restricted to calcareous soil; man orchid *Aceras anthropophorum*, uncommon, Hampshire and Somerset where rediscovered near Bath; bee orchid *Ophrys apifera*, declining but sometimes locally plentiful; dwarf orchid *Orchis ustulata*, very local but widespread; spotted orchid *Dactylorchis fuchsii*, well-distributed; pyramidal orchid *Anacamptis pyramidalis*, widespread and locally common.

A number of very local and rare flowers grow on the chalk. The round-headed rampion *Phyteuma tenerum* does not apparently occur in Berkshire or Dorset but it is locally frequent in Hampshire and north Wiltshire. The yellow-wort *Blackstonia perfoliata* is another local species found particularly on deep calcareous soils. The beautiful pasque flower *Anemone pulsatilla* grows in several places on the Berkshire downs. On these downs also, and just over the border in north-west Hampshire, is found the rare Chiltern gentian *Gentianella germanica*. The English felwort *G. anglica* and the autumn gentian *G. amarella* are more widespread. The tuberous thistle *Cirsium tuberosum* is a rare plant of Wiltshire first discovered in 1812. Its status became uncertain following heavy ploughing in World War II but it still grows in a few places, as for instance, on the Marlborough Downs and on the downs above the Wylye valley although it frequently hybridises with *C. acaulon*. The Nottingham catchfly *Silene nutans* grows on Portsdown Hill in Hampshire and the purple milk-vetch *Astragalus danicus* occurs in Wiltshire.

The Lias rocks of the Polden Hills support a flora similar to that of the Mendips though more restricted and typical plants include the common rock rose, salad burnet, horseshoe vetch, English felwort and woolly-headed thistle.

As is to be expected there are many snails on the chalk and limestone since calcium is needed for the construction of the shell. One of the most striking is the so-called Roman snail *Helix pomatia* which has been recorded from one north Hampshire locality and from a few places in north Wiltshire between Devizes and Marlborough.

Several species of short-horned grasshoppers such as *Omocestus viridulus* and *Chorthippus brunneus* are common on the chalk hillsides. Dorset is particularly well favoured and the stripe-winged grasshopper *Stenobothrus lineatus*, usually a local species, is notably common in Purbeck. *Gomphocerippus rufus* is also typical of dry habitats and is found on chalk slopes in south Hampshire, Berkshire, Dorset and north Somerset.

Butterflies are a colourful feature of the downs in summer. Cyclical fluctuations are a feature of butterfly life but there is no doubt at all that the decline, and in some cases disappearance, of butterflies from the downs since World War II has been due to the loss of habitat caused through conversion of downland to arable fields. Excellent localities for downland butterflies in the region are Wiltshire, with its extensive mass of chalk, and the Isle of Purbeck in Dorset.

The blues and the skippers are the two especially typical groups, although not all of them are confined to this habitat. The small blue *Cupido minimus* is widely, if somewhat locally, distributed and although reported rare in north Somerset, strong colonies exist in such places as the quarries of Purbeck, the downs around Salisbury, Ladle Hill near Newbury and the north Berkshire downs. The common blue *Polyommatus icarus* is most abundant of the blues, and the brown argus *Aricia agestis* is generally common. The chalkhill blue *Lysandra coridon* and the adonis blue *L. bellargus* are pre-eminently butterflies of downland for the caterpillars feed on horseshoe vetch. *Lysandra coridon* is noted for the frequency of its colour aberrations, and is the more common of the two though in recent years its status appears to be fluctuating greatly; whilst many areas have reported a great decrease a few have actually recorded an increase and the species is still locally common in Wiltshire. The adonis is a handsome insect which must now be classified as rare. Its distribution at the present time is restricted to a few favoured localities.

Among the skippers, the silver-spotted *Hesperia comma* is the only one of its family restricted to downland where it haunts the areas of short turf as opposed to the rough grassland. Once locally common it has declined greatly and some districts are reporting it extinct. In recent years the Essex skipper *Thymelicus lineola* which for so long was thought to be restricted to south-east England has been discovered to be locally common in south Wiltshire. Of the remaining members of the family, the grizzled *Pyrgus malvae*, the dingy *Erynnis tages*, the small *Thymelicus sylvestris* and the large *Ochlodes venata* are fairly common and widespread.

The marbled white *Melanargia galathea* is a beautiful butterfly locally abundant in areas of rough calcareous grassland. One normally associates the grayling *Eumenis semele* with the sandy soil of heathland but local colonies exist on the chalk and it is interesting to note a tendency for these downland forms to be whiter on the underside. A similar duality of habitat occurs with the dark green fritillary *Argynnis aglaia* although so far as I know no colour change takes place with this species. Two small butterflies, the small copper *Lycaena phlaeas* and the small heath *Coenonympha pamphilus*, are usually common and widespread on the dry slopes of the downs. Mention should also be made of two locally common species, the marsh fritillary *Euphydryas aurinia* and the Duke of Burgundy fritillary *Hamearis lucina*. At first it seems surprising that a marsh insect should be found on hillsides, but the fact is that it has two entirely different habitats with one factor in common and that is the presence of its food plant, devil's bit *Scabiosa succisa*. Colonies of this butterfly are found along the line of the Berkshire Ridgeway, on the downs around Blandford in Dorset and on the hills above the Vale of Pewsey.

The decline in the butterflies of the chalk is paralleled by that of the moths, many of which are less common than they used to be. Characteristic species of this habitat include the chalk carpet *Ortholitha bipunctaria* which frequents the areas of short turf and exposed chalk, the tawny shears *Hadena lepida*, the shears *H. nana*, the marbled coronet *H. conspersa* and the straw underwing *Thalpophila matura*. The grey chi *Antitype chi* is a species of northern distribution which has been recorded from Dorset and north Wiltshire. A rare moth of the Kentish downs, the feathered ear *Pachetra sagittigera*, is found also in south-east Wiltshire although it is very rare there.

Some moths of the downs fly in the sunshine. Such include the five- and six-spot burnet *Zygaena infolii* and *Z. filipendulae*, the light-feathered rustic *Agrotis denticulatus*, the wood tiger *Parasemia plantaginis* and the small purple-barred *Phytometra viridaria*. Two very local moths of the genus *Procris* occur in Wiltshire. The aptly named scarce forester *P. globulariae* is a rare insect of southern England which flies in only a few places on the downs although the food plant, knapweed, is common enough. The cistus forester *P. geryon* is rather more common in Wiltshire where the larvae feed on rock rose.

The hillocks of the yellow ant *Acanthomyops flavus* are a typical feature of many a chalk down, and the interrelationships of the plant and animal life of these anthills make a fascinating study, the acid soil enabling calcifuge plants to grow, the summits providing convenient places for rabbits to deposit their dung and the ant pupae supplying food for green woodpeckers.

A good variety of beetles, including ground beetles and plant feeders, live on downland. The bombardier beetle *Brachinus crepitans* and the bloody-nosed beetles *Timarcha tenebricosa* and *T. goettingensis* are typical of the chalk although somewhat local. The glow-worm *Lampyris noctiluca* attracts the attention even of those who are not coleopterists. It is probably not as common as it used to be. A very rare glow-worm *Phosphaenus hemipterus* has been recorded from Hampshire. The Fonthill grottoes in Wiltshire are artificial caves harbouring several species of bat including greater and lesser horseshoes and natterers. The cave spider *Meta menardi* is also found here. Slow-worms and grass snakes are generally common and widely distributed on the hills.

Birds typical of chalk down have decreased in recent years. The wheatear is now almost extinct as a breeder on the downs and in the case of this species an additional adverse factor was the arrival of myxomatosis in the rabbit for they often nest in rabbit burrows. Stone curlews have the same sad story of decrease to tell, but they still breed in the mainland counties of the region with the exception of Somerset, being perhaps most plentiful on the north Hampshire and Berkshire downs. Before the autumn migration they tend to congregate at favourite gathering grounds, Quarley Hill in Hampshire being one such spot. The skylark is the common bird of the downs, its sustained melody from on high on a spring day contrasting with the drone of the tractors below. The yellowhammer is common too, but its close relative the cirl bunting is more local although scattered through the region in, for instance, the neighbourhood of Bath, the south Somerset hills, the vicinity of Swanage in Dorset and some parts of the Hampshire downs. The corn bunting is locally plentiful in some parts and its breeding areas include central and eastern Hampshire, central Wiltshire (I have found them particularly common in the Vale of Pewsey), Purbeck and Portland in Dorset and the Lambourne Downs in Berkshire. Kestrels are often seen hovering over the slopes; hen harriers are sporadic winter visitors, but short-eared owls are fairly regular in winter and have even nested in Wiltshire in recent years.

Up to the nineteenth century great bustards roamed the chalk uplands of southern England, particularly Salisbury Plain where the last pair bred in 1806, although individual birds were seen sometime after this and vagrants have been reported in winter from time to time. The last bird seen in Somerset was at Shapwick on 27 September 1870. An interesting project is under way to re-establish the great bustard as a breeding species on Salisbury Plain, and several birds are being acclimatised on a 10 acre reserve in western Hampshire on the eastern edge of the plain. Everyone must hope that this scheme will be successful but previous attempts in past years have failed.

There is some evidence that birds migrate along the Wiltshire and Berkshire downs rather than the valleys. This migration consists not only of coasting along the scarp face but also of broad front movements trending south-westwards, following the general direction of the geological strata although tributary streams feed the main migrating mass. That elusive wader of the Scottish high tops, the dotterel, is seldom seen on passage in southern England but it used regularly to follow this downland route northward during the spring migration. Then early this century it became apparent that for some unaccountable reason it was no longer using this route. It was therefore of much interest to learn of four dotterel which were seen just north of the Berkshire/Oxfordshire border in the spring of 1971, presumably having once again taken the traditional route.

Chalk scrub

Chalk grassland if left alone proceeds to scrub. If conservationists wish to preserve the downland habitat they therefore either have to introduce sheep grazing or plan a regular maintenance programme of uprooting shrubs.

Juniper *Juniperus communis* is a scarce shrub growing on warm south-facing chalk slopes. The larvae of two moths, the juniper pug *Eupithecia sobrinata* and the juniper carpet *Thera juniperata*, feed on the leaves. The former is widespread but the latter, within the region, occurs only in Berkshire.

On deeper soils a mixed community of mainly calcicolous shrubs develop. Hawthorn *Crataegus monogyna* is a common and early coloniser which provides food and shelter for a wealth of insect life. Climbing over this and other shrubs is the old man's beard *Clematis vitalba*, abundant and a certain indicator of calcareous soil. Some insects are specific to this climber; they include the pretty chalk carpet *Melanthia procellata*, Haworth's pug *Eupithecia haworthiata*, the small waved umber *Horisme vitalbata*, the fern *H. tersata* and the small emerald *Hemistola immaculata*, all fairly common in the region.

The spindle *Euonymus europaeus* stands out in the autumn with its attractive coral-red and orange berries and colourful foliage on which feed the larvae of the scorched carpet *Ligdia adustata*. Dogwood *Thelycrania sanguinea*, another common shrub, provides food for many insects. Buckthorn *Rhamnus catharticus* is occasional and is the food plant for the caterpillars of the brown scallop moth *Philereme vitulata*. The wayfaring tree *Viburnum lantana* is plentiful and not only has a number of insects specifically associated with it but attracts many others which range over a wide spectrum of plants. The orange-tailed clearwing *Aegeria andrenaeformis* is recorded from Dorset and the Berkshire downs and the larvae live in the stems of the wayfaring tree. An aphis *Aphis lantanae*, a micromoth *Lithocolletis lantanella* and a leaf beetle *Galerucella viburni* are specific to this shrub.

Green hairstreak butterflies *Callophrys rubi* are fairly common in chalk scrub although not easy to see because of their coloration. Various bush crickets are found in this habitat.

The Mendips

This hill range consists of Carboniferous Limestone. Much of the chalk flora grows on this also so that here reference will be made only to those species especially characteristic of this district. It can be said straight away that the Mendips have a rich variety of flowers. The soil overlying limestone is often deeper and moister than the shallow chalk rendzinas. *Festuca* pastures have spring cinquefoil *Potentilla tabernaemontani* as a common component, and the ox-eye daisy *Chrysanthemum leucanthemum* is a conspicuous feature in summer. Typical plants of the rocks include madder *Rubia peregrina*, pellitory of the wall *Parietaria diffusa*, pennywort *Umbilicus rupestris*, rock stonecrop *Sedum forsteranum* and lesser meadow rue *Thalictrum minus*. Two northern species, mossy saxifrage *Saxifraga hypnoides* and a fern, the limestone polypody *Thelypteris robertiana*, occur, the former reaching here its most southerly site in the country. Two coastal species are also found here, the sea campion *Silene maritima* and the sea stork's bill *Erodium maritimum*, perhaps relict plants from the time in the geologically recent past when Mendip was a sea cliff. The two rarities of Brean Down mentioned in Chapter Two (page 62), mountain rock rose and Somerset grass, grow also in the western part of the ridge. It is remarkable that this grass was first discovered and described as long ago as 1726 by an Oxford professor of botany and was not recognised again until this century.

Cheddar gorge is a happy hunting ground for botanists with its well known Cheddar pink *Dianthus gratianopolitanus* and its other less well known endemic plants, two species of hawkweed, but this genus with its 216 species can safely be left to the specialists. Welsh poppy *Meconopsis cambrica* and limestone polypody grow on the screes. Lady's mantle *Alchemilla vestita* is abundant and the local cut-leaved self-heal *Prunella laciniata* and bloody cranesbill *Geranium sanguineum* grow here. The term 'gruffy ground' is used by Mendip dwellers to describe the rough uneven ground of the disused lead mines and it has been frequently noted that alpine pennycress *Thlaspi alpestre* and vernal sandwort *Minuarta verna* are especially characteristic of this habitat.

A feature of Carboniferous Limestone country is the cave and underground river system. The Mendips have many such caves and a specialised fauna inhabits them. In glacial times they sheltered the brown bear, wolf, lynx, hyena and reindeer. They still continue to provide a home for animals although these are now minute in size compared with the giants of the past. Considerable numbers of those tiny primitive insects the springtails live within the first sixty yards of a cave entrance but very few penetrate further. They include some half-dozen species adapted to a cave existence and never found outside. In one of them, *Onychiurus fimetarius*, the adaptation is so complete that it is both white and blind. Mosquitoes, craneflies and several darkness-loving species of beetles are found. The cave spider which was mentioned earlier in this chapter as occurring in the Fonthill grottoes lives also in the Mendip caves together with another of the same genus *Meta merianae*. A tiny wingless fly which resembles a spider and which is parasitic on bats is *Nycteribia biarticulata*. These live on the whiskered, lesser and greater horseshoe bats which are the largest of the cave dwellers in the Mendips in these days.

Emerging into the light of day we find a good range of butterflies with marbled white, brown argus, green hairstreak, and several skippers including the Essex skipper, but the chalkhill and adonis blues have become very rare.

The ravens, peregrines, blackgame, red-backed shrike and woodlark which once bred on the Mendips are there no more, but the disused quarries still hold kestrels and jackdaws and the buzzard has made a successful come-back. From World War I onward it has gradually spread from the west until now it is well-established in north Somerset although it suffered a temporary set-back with the advent of myxomatosis and the disappearance of the rabbit, its principal food. The two common birds of the hill pastures are skylarks and meadow pipits. Of the buntings, the yellowhammer is plentiful but the corn bunting and cirl bunting are local. In the lower eastern part of the Mendips the tree sparrow breeds; this is another bird which has shown a welcome increase in recent years.

Page 107 (*above*) The uncommon Dorset heath growing amongst gorse in the Isle of Purbeck; (*below left*) gorse weevil *Apion ulicis*; (*below right*) kestrel eating prey at Durlston Head, Swanage

Page 108 (*above*) Linnet's nest; (*below*) field corners left uncultivated for wild life on the farm of Mr P. Smith at Purtington, Somerset

The Quantocks

South-west of Bridgwater the Quantock Hills lie diagonally athwart the route westward to Devon, the outermost bastion guarding the approach to Exmoor.

Looking from the Quantocks on a clear day one can see the Mendips 24 miles away to the north-east. Both ranges are similar in length and height and both have coniferous plantations but there the resemblance ends. The Quantocks consist of rocks of Old Red Sandstone age, chiefly indurated sandstone known as Hangman's Grits with some slates and a little limestone of Devonian age. The range is dissected by beautiful combes, some of which have now been planted with conifers which have inevitably changed their character. Before this they were still partially wooded but, like the rest, with deciduous trees of which the sessile oak is the commonest species, although there are some beech, birch, holly, rowan and ash. These combes are delightful places in which to walk, especially in spring when the snowdrops, celandines and bluebells follow each other in quick succession. Good crops of fungi occur in favourable seasons and ferns are plentiful.

There is some resemblance to the more hilly parts of the New Forest, a likeness which is heightened when, climbing past patches of bilberry and broom, one reaches the higher levels to find the vast expanse of bracken and ling dotted with clumps of Welsh gorse and hawthorn. Cowberry *Vaccinium vitis-idaea* was discovered growing here in 1917 and rediscovered after a long interval in 1958. The Cornish moneywort *Sibthorbia europaea* is another distinguished member of the Quantock flora.

On the flowers of bilberry feed the bilberry or mountain humble bee *Bombus lapponicus*, a distinctly local species of high ground mainly in the north and west of the country; apart from the Quantocks it has been seen at one place in the Mendips where the Old Red Sandstone comes to the surface.

Scattered on the open moor are boggy depressions and in one

of them grow a few plants of the Irish butterwort *Pinguicula grandiflora*. The summit moorland has much the same lepidoptera as a lowland heath; dark green fritillaries, graylings and small heaths in the butterflies and among the moths the emperor *Saturnia pavonia* in April followed by the wildly careering fox moth *Macrothylacia rubi* in June. The beautiful snout *Bomolocha fontis* is fairly common, the larvae feeding on bilberry.

The bracken-covered slopes are good haunts for adder and common lizard. Walking one day near Will's Neck I met a small boy who ran up to me excitedly, eager to show me an adder which he had just seen. His glad willingness to share the good things of nature I wholeheartedly endorse, and it is for me a matter of regret that in the case of a few of the rarer species I have felt obliged, in this imperfect world, to be rather vague about localities elsewhere in this book.

Although meadow pipits are plentiful other birds of the moorland have either ceased to breed or declined greatly. Some whinchats still nest but stonechats are scarce and red-backed shrikes and wheatears probably no longer breed. Kestrels and buzzards, however, are often seen.

The combes hold a richer animal life. There are the four species of woodland fritillaries and many kinds of moth. Grass snakes, slow-worms, foxes and badgers are common. Mention will be made in a later chapter of the herd of red deer. The red squirrel is now extinct; the Quantocks were probably its last stronghold on the mainland of this region.

Apart from the more usual woodland birds, redstarts and tree pipits are regular breeders and pied flycatchers and lesser redpolls occasionally nest; in fact the last-named, although local, have increased in Somerset in recent years and may now nest regularly on the Quantocks. Ring ouzels are birds of passage. Of the Corvid family ravens occasionally nest. A bird which threatens to join the red squirrel in extinction is the black grouse which was common here this century until about 1950. Only a handful now remain. The north-facing combes with their rhododendron thickets must have been an ideal habitat for them and I suspect that heavy afforestation is at least partly responsible for the decrease since the black grouse, like that other declining species the woodlark, is a bird of open woodland or woodland edge.

CHAPTER FIVE

Woodland

Mixed deciduous woods—Beech woods—Ash woods—Coniferous plantations—Deer

AT THE DAWN of the historic period vast areas of southern England were thickly clothed with forests. In addition, much of the remainder was liberally studded with thickets of thorn. To-day, where physical conditions permit, and where human interference is negligible, plant succession proceeds in ordered steps to woodland. The natural climax of plant cover on the heavy loams and clays of southern England, for example, is oakwood.

But human interference has been *far* from negligible over the greater part of this region. For hundreds of years an unrelenting process of destruction has reduced the mighty forests to scattered remnants. Yet anyone arriving in the central southern region from northern Britain is immediately impressed by the numbers of trees that remain, in hedgerow, coppice and larger tracts of woodland. In the present century, too, the Forestry Commission has been active, although mainly in planting coniferous rather than broad-leaved trees.

The fragmentation of the forests has not been all loss to wild life. Relatively few plants and animals live in the dark depths of a wood; the edges and clearings are much more favoured. One of the effects of tree felling, then, has been to make a lineal increase in a desirable type of woodland habitat. When a wood is acquired as a nature reserve one of the principal aims of the management plan must be to provide such clearings.

Planning legislation enables a Tree Preservation Order to be made on individual trees or groups of trees: these orders are normally made on amenity grounds but it would be good if they were also made to preserve wild life when, for example, a colony of insects is based on a particular tree. I have in mind a colony of the white-letter hairstreak *Strymonidia w-album* which is centred on a tree in a Berkshire village, and another in a tree at Weston-super-Mare; but there must be a number of such cases.

The most heavily wooded county in the region is Hampshire, with trees covering 16 per cent of the total land area. The most sparsely wooded county is Somerset with only 5·5 per cent cover. Dorset is the only county in the region where the acreage of conifer plantations exceeds that of deciduous woodland; in Wiltshire the proportion of deciduous woods is much larger.

Mixed deciduous woods

Pure communities with a single tree species are rare and this section will cover not only areas in which the pedunculate oak *Quercus robur* is the dominant species but also mixed deciduous woodland.

Ground layer. Generally a deciduous wood consists of a four-tier structure although in places one or more tiers may be absent. There is first of all a moss, fungi and leaf-litter layer. Over twenty species of mosses occur in the oakwoods of southern England but none is limited to this habitat although many prefer acid conditions. Common and widespread species include *Thuidium tamariscinum*, *Brachythecium rutabulum* and *Mnium undulatum*.

In a favourable season these mixed deciduous woods produce a large and varied crop of fungi and the annual autumnal fungus forays of the local natural history societies are usually well-patronised by their members. The stinkhorn *Phallus impudicus* is more often smelt than seen but is generally common. Where forest workers have had bonfires the resultant burnt patches produce their own distinctive plant life, the fungi *Collybia atrata* and *Flammula carbonaria* and a moss *Funaria hygrometrica*. A tiny beetle is associated with these burnt patches; this is *Acritus homoeopathicus*, in this region known only from Dorset. In the genus *Lactarius*, *L. quietus* is characteristic of oak woods as is the appropriately-named *Marasmius dryophilus*. Other fungi occurring plentifully in the region include *Russula* spp, *Boletus* spp especially *B. chrysenteron*, *Lycoperdon* spp, *Amanita* spp including the notorious deathcap *A. phalloides* and *Laccaria laccata* with its attractive violet form *amethystina*.

Herb layer. Whilst there is a considerable variety of flowering plants in oak woods there are some particularly characteristic basic constituents. This basic element itself depends on whether the soil is wet or dry. Woods on heavy loams are at their most attractive in early spring, when the yellow of primrose *Primula vulgaris* and lesser celandine *Ranunculus ficaria*, followed by the fresh white of wood anemone *Anemone nemorosa*, colour the woodland floor. Dog's mercury *Mercurialis perennis* is often dominant over large areas, and stinging nettle *Urtica dioica*, dog violet *Viola riviniana*, herb robert *Geranium robertianum*, enchanter's nightshade *Circaea lutetiana*, the speedwells *Veronica* spp and foxglove *Digitalis purpurea* are other very common species.

Clearings provide scope for the rosebay willow herb *Chamaenerion angustifolium* to rampage and here in these felled areas grows a much greater variety of flowers than under the shade of the trees. Species that grow in spindly fashion in small numbers in the shade here thrive in robust colonies. Sometimes grasses are dominant in the more open areas and I do not recall a more luxuriant growth of the tufted hair grass *Deschampsia caespitosa* than that seen in the open areas of Clifton Wood in Dorset.

On sandy soils the emphasis is rather different. Here in May the sheets of bluebell *Endymion non-scriptus* are on so vast and colourful a scale that even those who are normally oblivious of botanical delights make weekend pilgrimages to admire and, alas, to pick. Often associated with them is creeping soft grass *Holcus mollis*, and bracken *Pteridium aquilinum* grows in greater abundance on these lighter soils.

Interesting local or uncommon plants occur in mixed deciduous woods within the region. Herb paris *Paris quadrifolia* is found locally distributed in oakwoods especially on calcareous soils, occurring for example, in hazel coppices on the Dorset limestone and in certain woods on the chalk in the Hampshire uplands, in woods around Salisbury and in south-west Berkshire. The lily of the valley *Convallaria majalis* grows sparsely in similar situations and is locally abundant in north Somerset woods. The autumn crocus *Colchicum autumnale* which grows in Savernake Forest and in the Carboniferous Limestone woods of Somerset, and columbine *Aquilegia vulgaris* are other scarce constitutents of oakwood flora on calcareous soils although the latter is not confined to this habitat.

Shrub layer. Hazel is the shrub of oakwood. The reason for this comesfrom the practice of growing hazel in coppices with oaks as standards amongst them. Hazel coppices are known to have been cultivated in southern England as early as the fifteenth century. Every few years the stems were cut and used for charcoal and for the construction of wattle and daub dwellings. By the nineteenth century hazel was being cut for pea and bean sticks and for wattle fencing. The practice of coppicing has fallen into disuse because it is not economic forestry and the oak standards produced by this method do not make as good timber as that which is grown in close canopy.

Hawthorn *Crataegus monogyna*, blackthorn *Prunus spinosa* and dog rose *Rosa canina* are other common shrubs; climbers are represented by honeysuckle *Lonicera periclymenum*, bramble *Rubus fruticosus* and ivy *Hedera helix*. On basic soils guelder rose *Viburnum opulus*, wayfaring tree *V. lantana*, spindle *Euonymus europaeus*, dogwood *Thelycrania sanguinea* and privet *Ligustrum vulgare* are often constitutents of the shrub layer. On heavy soils sallows *Salix* spp are common.

The dominant tree of the canopy is the pedunculate oak associated with a number of others, including ash *Fraxinus excelsior*, maple *Acer campestre*, sycamore *Acer pseudoplatanus*, gean *Prunus avium*, birch *Betula* spp, holly *Ilex aquifolium*, rowan *Sorbus aucuparia*, grey poplar *Populus canescens*, aspen *Populus tremula*, English elm *Ulmus procera*, and small-leaved lime *Tilia cordata*.

Sessile oak *Q. sessiliflora* also occurs on Plateau Gravel in parts of the Pang Valley in Berkshire, is plentiful in the Avon gorge, and in the Quantocks it is the commonest species.

Fauna. The ground layer is occupied by enormous numbers of invertebrates. They include earthworms, bristle-tails, spring-tails, mites, spiders, wood-lice, millipedes, centipedes, false-scorpions, ants, beetles, bugs, slugs and snails. Many of these classes, however, do not attract the attention of the field naturalist. Yet he cannot fail to see the abundant large black slug *Arion Ater* along the woodland rides, and will be familiar with the ground beetles of the family Carabidae as they run across the path seeking their prey. An uncommon species of ground beetle found in oakwoods is *Calosoma inquisitor*, of a shining green and copper colour. The plaited snail *Acanthinula lamellata* is very scarce in southern England but lives in deciduous woods in eastern Berkshire. A rare British snail known as the cheese snail, *Helicodonta obvoluta*, occurs within the region in the vicinity of Petersfield in Hampshire, and the mountain bulin *Ena montana*, a very local species, in a wood on the eastern Mendips. Of the ground-haunting members of the Orthoptera, the common ground-hopper *Tetrix undulata* is widely distributed; the indigenous cockroach *Ectobius lividus* occurs in Hampshire and Berkshire, and the wood cricket *Nemobius sylvestris* is a local species found in south Hampshire, south Wiltshire and Dorset. Wolf spiders *Lycosa* spp are conspicuous, and at the other end of the scale are the tiny money spiders of the family *Linyphiidae*.

Of the smaller mammals, moles, bank voles and long-tailed field mice are generally common. Dormice are more elusive creatures, but occur locally in hazel coppice. They are recorded from various woods in the vicinity of Salisbury, in the Reading area and in south Somerset where they are fairly common. It is estimated that their populations have to withstand an 80 per cent mortality during the hibernation period.

Foxes are numerous and badgers, although regrettably still persecuted in some places, are more than holding their own. Various surveys of the distribution of badger setts show that deciduous woodland is the favourite site. Within this habitat there is a preference for slopes, and for a relatively soft stratum such as limestone (including chalk) and sand, as shown on page 118. Within this preference pattern badgers are common throughout the region, particularly in south Hampshire, south-west and central Wiltshire, the Isle of Purbeck, the Mendips, the Poldens, the district around Bath and the Blackdown Hills of south Somerset. An excellent idea of the Forestry Commission is the provision of badger gates (illustrated on page 89). The forester uses the badger's habit of following a regular track out of a plantation, and gives him a small swing gate which he can push open, thus avoiding damage to the fence. Badger hides have been erected by some local naturalists' trusts for the use of their members in woodland reserves.

A great wealth of animal life, especially invertebrate, lives in oakwood, feeding on flowers, shrubs and the oaks themselves. Mention can be made only of the more conspicuous creatures and specialities of the region.

Violets provide food for the caterpillars of the fritillaries *Argynnis* spp. Small pearl-bordered *A. selene* are probably less common than the pearl-bordered *A. euphrosyne* but both occur in small colonies. The large blocks of woodland usually hold the two larger species, the high brown *A. cydippe* and the silver-washed *A. paphia.* One of the commonest woodland butterflies is the speckled wood *Pararge aegeria* the larvae of which with those of the ringlet *Aphantopus hyperanthus*, a more local species, feed on the grasses of the rides. The little Duke of Burgundy fritillary *Hamearis lucina* appears patchily distributed.

Honeysuckle is the larval food plant of that fine insect the white admiral *Limenitis camilla* which in some seasons is quite plentiful, in others scarce; it has spread westwards into Somerset

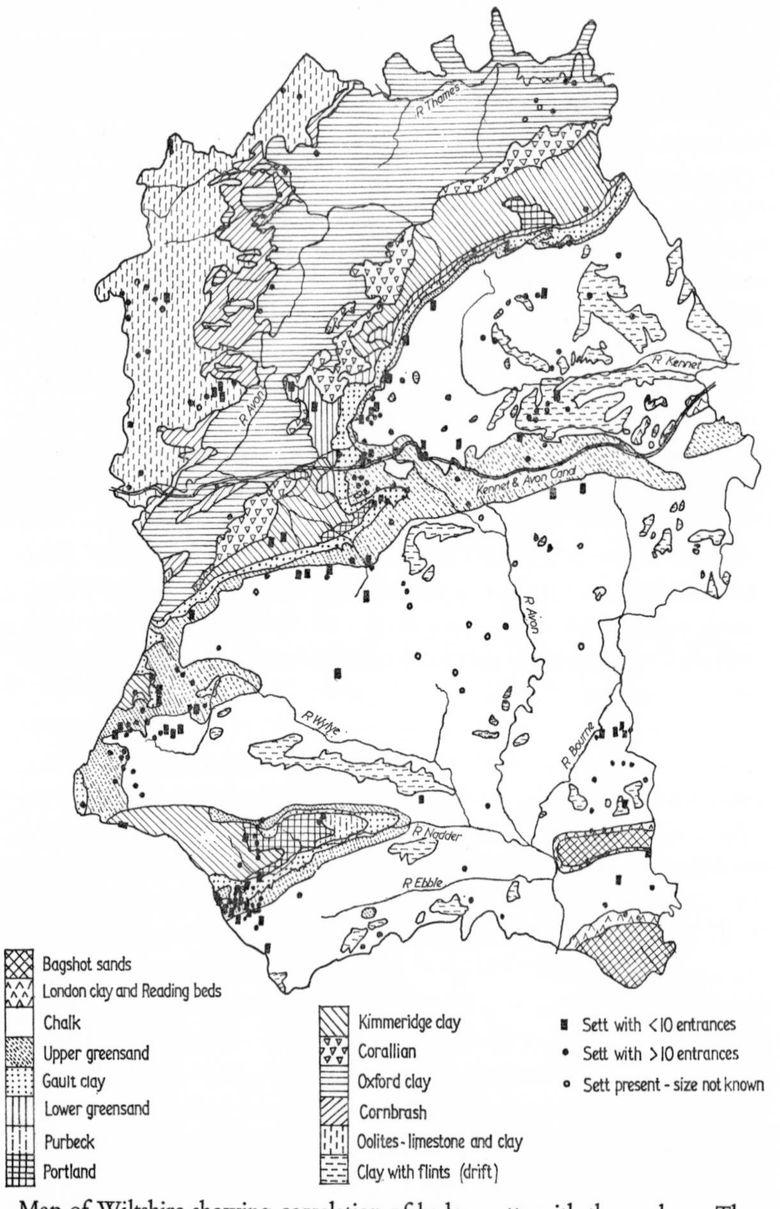

Map of Wiltshire showing correlation of badger setts with the geology. The higher proportion of setts on the Greensand is clearly shown. After Miss B. Gillam from *1966 Natural History Report* of the Wiltshire Archaeological and Natural History Society. Crown copyright. Based on Geological Survey map. Reproduced by permission of Director, IGS but as yet is uncommon in that county. Fine as the white admiral is, it is surpassed by the magnificent purple emperor *Apatura iris* which requires a juxtaposition of sallow and oak, the former for the caterpillar and the latter for the imago. It is scarce throughout the region but occurs in a north Hampshire forest, in relatively small patches of woodland in the Reading area, and in various woods on the Hampshire–Wiltshire border; and in 1969 it was seen again in north Somerset after an absence of 51 years. The Wiltshire Trust for Nature Conservation is taking active steps in one reserve to provide and maintain the right type of habitat. A large purple emperor detaching itself from the crown of an oak tree on the edge of a clearing and with majestic flight circling the oak for a few seconds is a never-to-be-forgotten sight.

Purple hairstreaks *Thecla querca* are also to be seen around the upper branches of oaks in July and are widely distributed. The wood white *Leptidea sinapis* is a somewhat fragile-looking, shade-loving butterfly, scarce in the region generally but fairly common in south Somerset. In the rides fly various species such as green-veined white *Pieris napi* and several of the skippers, particularly the small skipper *Thymelicus sylvestris* and the large skipper *Ochlodes venata.*

Moths of many species abound in mixed deciduous woodland and the oak is the larval food plant of more species than any other tree. In the ground under oaks may be dug up the pupae of the merveille de jour *Griposia aprilina*, an attractive green moth. Another beautiful green moth is the green silver-line *Bena prasinana* and, much more local, the scarce silver-line *Pseudoips bicolorana*, which is found in the eastern part of the region. Three of the pugs are oak feeders, oaktree *Eupithecia dodoneata*, marbled *E. irriguata* and brindled *E. abbreviata*, the last named being recorded as particularly common in Somerset. A contrast in size is the great oak beauty *Boarmia roborana*, the more local pale oak beauty *B. punctinalis* and the oak beauty *Biston strataria*, found in some of the larger woods.

A rather delicate green grasshopper, the oak bush cricket

Meconema thalassinum, is found in all the counties of the region. This is the only tree-haunting grasshopper in Britain. In old woodland, such as Windsor Forest, hornets *Vespa crabro* build their intimidating nests in hollow trees. Also in Windsor and the neighbouring areas occurs another and much rarer Hymenopteron, the brown tree ant *Acanthomyops brunneus*, the only British ant which lives and makes its nest in the upper branches of trees, though other species forage up tree trunks.

Oakwoods are inhabited, many people might say infested, with millions of flies. Most of these are small and of interest only to the dipterist but a few compel attention either by their size, noise, colouring or unwelcome persistence. On a hot summer's day the walker in a deciduous wood is likely to be closely followed by a dense swarm of flies, not biting but attracted by human perspiration. This insect is *Hydrotaea irritans* and its presence can make a day in the woods unpleasant. Unfortunately a small minority of flies do bite: the midges of the family *Ceratopogonidae* always seem more active in a humid atmosphere or after rain, and although tiny they can certainly make themselves felt. There are many others, the mosquitoes, the black flies, the attractive *Chrysops* spp with their irridescent eyes, the duller *Haematopoda* spp and of course the Tabanids, large biting flies common in the oakwoods of southern England. Not infrequently the walker will hear a menacing hum as a large insect circles him repeatedly at incredible speed. It travels so fast that it is difficult to get any impression of its shape or colour but the noise induces respect. It could be a hornet, but it is more likely to be one of the largest of the Tabanids, of which there are three closely related species, about an inch in length. Strangely enough, although these can inflict a formidable bite they do not seem so aggressive as some of their smaller relatives. Woods in the region are usually well populated with the interesting and often beautiful Syrphid flies which hover over flower heads. Many of them mimic bees and wasps in their coloration and some of the genus *Volucella* live whilst in the larval state in the nests of bees.

Some rare flies occur: the large and strikingly handsome

Syrphid *Calliprobola speciosa* is found in old woodland such as Windsor Forest, and here is also a rare stilt-legged fly *Rainieria calceata*. Bagley wood just south of Oxford is a famous entomological locality which has produced a number of rarities. *Agria mamillata*, a very rare parasitic fly, and species new to Britain such as the midge *Diamesia galadoptera* have been discovered there.

In nests of the brown tree ant at Windsor several rare beetles have been found, a weevil *Dryopthorus corticalis* and two 'staphs', *Batrisodes delaportei* and *B. adnexus*. The magnificent stag beetle *Lucanus cervus* is rather scarce and its two close relatives hardly less so. They occur in tree stumps as do the brilliantly coloured cardinal beetles *Pyrochroa* spp. The common cockchafer *Melolontha melolontha* is widespread, the summer chafer *Amphimallon solstitialis* is more local and *Amphimallon ochraceus* is a rare chafer recorded from Berkshire. Reference has been made to the mimicking of Hymenopterons by certain Syrphid flies and here the wasp beetle *Clytus arietis*, common and widespread within the region, should be mentioned.

Plant bugs of many species abound in oakwoods, not only on the trees but also on all the associated plants, many of them being specific to a particular species of flower. On the oaks are the forest shield-bug *Pentatoma rufipes*, the small *Anthocoris confusus*, the handsome black and yellow *Dryophilocoris flavoquadrimaculatus* and *Cyllecoris histrionicus*.

Spiders too, occur in immense numbers in deciduous woodland. Many of them are found in the lower vegetation, but species such as *Clubiona brevipes* and *Anyphaena accentuata* are abundant on trees. *Cyclosa conica* and *Theridion lunatum* are true woodland species because they are found more especially in the darker parts of the wood. Bagley Wood in Berkshire is the only station for *Theridion pulchellum*, and *Tuberta moerens* which occurs here has only been recorded from one other place. Wytham Woods, also in Berkshire, is the only known locality within the region for *Zygiella stroemi*. In this wood numbers of the rare pirate spider *Pirata uliginosus* were discovered in 1961 amongst bracken. In a jackdaw's nest in Windsor Forest was located the spider *Lepthyphantes carri*, found nowhere else in the region.

Bats, though they also occur in caves and buildings, are primarily woodland creatures. Much remains unknown even about their distribution. Certainly, however, central southern England is rich in species. The common and widespread bats are the noctule *Nyctalus noctula*, pipistrelle *Pipistrellus pipistrellus*, whiskered *Myotis mysticinus*, Daubenton's *Myotis daubentoni* and long-eared *Plecotus auritus*. The greater and lesser horseshoes *Rhinolophus ferrum-equinum* and *R. hipposideros* are locally plentiful; the former has an ecclesiastical preference, roosting in Wells and Winchester cathedrals. Natterer's *Myotis natteri* is fairly common and the barbastelle *Barbastella barbastellus* is reported from along the south coast. The serotine *Eptesicus serotinus* is locally abundant in Hampshire but becomes much scarcer further west. Leisler's *Nyctalus leisleri* is a rather uncommon bat which may, however, be more frequent than its distribution records suggest: it is recorded from the Meon Valley in Hampshire and in the Bristol area. Of the long-known British species Bechstein's *Myrtis bechsteini* is the rarest. It was first discovered in the New Forest in the early part of the last century, where it still occurs, and is known also in the Isle of Wight and other locations.

In recent years Dorset has been causing excitement by producing new species for the British list, although this may be partly due to Dorset being especially favoured with bat-watchers rather than with bats. In 1875 a grey long-eared bat *Plecotus austriacus* was killed at Netley, Hampshire, but it was not identified as such until 1964. Since then it has been recorded a number of times in Dorset. In 1957 the mouse-eared bat *Myrtis myotis* was found in Dorset and added to the British list. Then in the autumn of 1969 *Pipistrellus nathusii*, a European bat never before recorded in Britain, was found at the Furzebrook Nature Conservancy Research Station in Dorset. The bat was found to harbour its own specific parasite, the flea *Ischnopsyllus variabilis*.

Despite the continuous war waged against it the grey squirrel *Sciurus carolinensis* has the ability to overcome any temporary setback. Although originally an alien it has clearly found its ecological niche and is firmly established.

The bird population of woods varies with the seasons. In winter, very few birds remain. Wrens creep amongst the thick cover searching for hibernating insects, and blackbirds with their usual disproportionate amount of noise forage under the trees making the walker think momentarily that he has come upon some woodland mammal; a pheasant may rocket up from the ride with startling explosiveness; a tree-creeper or one of the other trunk-climbing species may be seen on the bole of a tree; parties of tits go foraging through the tree-tops and the raucous rasp of a jay may be heard. The only winter immigrants to be seen are wood pigeons with their noisy wing-clapping, and perhaps with good fortune a wintering woodcock, come in from the continent on the harvest moon. The distant hoot of a tawny owl at dusk completes the total of birds seen or heard.

Summer, when the woods come alive, is a rather different story, although even then the numbers of birds depend to some extent on whether the wood is open or close canopy, mature timber or a young plantation. An open wood with mature trees and many sunny glades has the highest bird population, as many birds prefer the edges of a wood and the clearings extend this habitat.

Chaffinches, and now bullfinches, are common and widespread. The hawfinch is a strange elusive bird difficult to locate and a great wanderer, turning up in unexpected places, in small numbers, in all the counties of the region. Three of the thrush family, blackbird, song thrush and missel thrush, are common nesting birds and the last named is on the increase. A few of the wintering woodcock stay to breed but they are scarce and are seldom if ever found on the chalk uplands. The stock dove is a resident, locally fairly common, and nests in holes in old trees although it is not confined to woodland since it also nests in rabbit burrows and quarries.

Certain resident birds are colonial nesters. The heron is a typical example. Some heronries have been established for many years but some are less permanent and the number of nests in each colony fluctuates considerably from year to year. In the crow family, jackdaws frequently nest in old woodland but rooks are more likely to be found in hedgerow trees or parkland. The carrion crow, which does not nest communally, builds its bulky nest of twigs in open woodland.

The tawny owl is the only member of its family normally found in oakwoods and it is widespread throughout the region. Amongst the birds of prey sparrow-hawks and kestrels are the two common species. The kestrel is more often seen but the sparrow-hawk is a more typically woodland bird. The sparrow-hawk population declined disastrously in the 1950s and 60s but since receiving protection, and since the voluntary ban on certain toxic chemicals, numbers have somewhat recovered. Buzzards are more numerous in the western part of the region but there is some evidence that they are extending their range eastwards. They are widespread in Somerset, Dorset and Wiltshire and have moved in to western Berkshire. In Hampshire, apart from their main stronghold in the New Forest, they are scarce and do not occur in the eastern part of the county. That handsome falcon the hobby is a summer migrant which breeds regularly in all the counties, with perhaps the greatest number in Hampshire where the distribution is similar to that of the buzzard, its scarcity in eastern Hampshire being odd because it is primarily a bird of south-eastern England, with a range extending westwards only to Devon.

Nuthatches and tree-creepers are common and widespread and the three species of woodpecker occur. The green woodpecker was severely hit by the hard winter of 1962–3 and has taken a long time to recover, but in the last two or three years has become much more plentiful. The barred or lesser spotted woodpecker must certainly be the least common of the three but it is locally distributed throughout the region.

Of the summer migrants, willow warblers, chiff-chaffs,

Page 125 (*above*) Aerial view of farm at Hammoon in the Blackmore Vale, the site of a farming and wild-life study in 1970; (*below*) great marsh grasshopper, an uncommon species of bogs in the New Forest and Dorset

Page 126 (*above*) Fallow bucks in the New Forest; (*below*) two vipers in a New Forest snake-pit, one the common colour form and the other a black variety

Green woodpecker by C. F. Tunnicliffe. Reproduced by courtesy of the Forestry Commission from their *New Forest Guide*

garden warblers, blackcaps and spotted flycatchers are plentiful and well distributed. The nightingale is especially associated with oak trees in that it frequently uses oak leaves for the construction of its nest. This is a species of south-eastern distribution and occurs more sparingly in Somerset; Leigh Woods in the Avon gorge is a well known locality for them and at Priors Park Wood they are considered to be at the western limit of their range. Further east they are locally common but in recent years a number of old haunts have been abandoned and there appears to be a decline in some areas. The redstart is a sparse breeder in woods with old trees; it is far from common in Dorset and Wiltshire; in Hampshire outside the New Forest it nests in a few places but in Somerset appears to be more plentiful, occurring in a number of localities including the Blackdown Hills, south of Taunton, and the Quantocks. Tree pipits are widespread but not abundant and require open woodland with clearings. The woodlark, like the tree pipit, requires open areas but this is a resident bird which has declined greatly in recent years. The Polden Hills with their tree-lined ridge were a stronghold of the species until this notable decline. The pied flycatcher is rare within the region, one or two pairs breeding occasionally in the Quantocks.

Leigh Woods are National Trust property sited on the Somerset side of the Avon gorge and worthy of special mention. Although the tree layer is varied, with sessile oak, ash, beech, birch and poplar, it has an interesting native tree common here and on the limestone elsewhere in the Bristol area. This is the small-leaved lime *Tilia cordata* which has its own distinctive fauna. The service tree *Sorbus torminalis* grows here, and scattered along the wooded slopes of the gorge are several rare species of whitebeam including one found nowhere else, *Sorbus bristoliensis*.

Well over 100 species of bryophytes have been recorded and the woods are well endowed with fungi. A rare fungus under the lime trees is *Arcangeliella stephensii*. The rich herb layer includes a number of local species on limestone such as dwarf chickweed *Cerastium pumilum*, narrow-leaved bitter cress *Cardamine impatiens* and fingered sedge *Carex digitata*.

These woods have long been noted for the abundance of their insect life. Extensive felling took place during World War II and there has since been considerable restocking with conifers. One hopes that the indigenous fauna will not be too much disturbed. This has been the only locality in Britain for the scarce hook-tip moth *Drepana harpigula*, the caterpillars of which feed on the lime. There is great doubt, however, whether the species exists there now. The white letter hairstreak is among the more interesting butterflies which are found there. The scarce Syrphid fly *Volucella inanis* whose larvae live in hornets' nests has been recorded from Leigh Woods.

Beechwoods

Beechwoods have a limited distribution within the region. Their requirements are a dry, well aerated soil, and outside the New Forest they are found mainly on the chalk. The principal areas are the steep hangers of the Hampshire downs, the south-western extension of the Chiltern beechwoods into north

Berkshire, Savernake Forest in Wiltshire, woods in north central Dorset and various scattered plantations.

The structure of a beechwood is quite different from that of oak. Beech casts heavy shade so that the field and shrub layers are greatly diminished. Despite the paucity of flowers beechwoods have a distinctive beauty of their own due principally to the translucency of the leaves which retain their interest the summer through, from the fresh silken green of spring to the bronze of autumn. If flowers are few there are nevertheless some interesting ones which are typical of this habitat.

Ground layer. The floor of the beechwood is a thick burnt-sienna carpet of leaf litter stained with random green patches of moss clumps. These mosses are of two kinds—those typical of calcareous soil and those calcifuge species which grow either in the beechwoods situated on sand or plateau gravel or on the acid surface humus in the woods on the chalk. *Eurhynchium striatum* and *E. praelongum* are typical species of the former, and *Mnium hornum* and *Dicranella heteromalla* are common, often abundant, species of the latter group. Round the base of beech trunks the mosses *Neckera complanata* and *Hypnum cupressiforme*, and a liverwort *Porella platyphylla*, are often found.

Although few mosses are linked with beech, some fungi are especially associated with it, including *Clitocybe clavipes*; *Marasmius* spp, on dead leaves; *Mycena* spp, on dead leaves; *Lactarius blennius* and *L. pallidus*. The boles of living beech sometimes bear the slimy white caps of *Armillaria mucida*. In 1966 in a wood near East Tisted, Hampshire, a rare species *Fomes fomentarius* was found. Until then it had been known in Britain only from the Scottish Highlands under birch, although on the continent it is a constituent of beechwoods.

Herb layer. The flowers of a close-canopied beechwood have to cope by some means or other with the deep shade. They do this either by early flowering—the plants in this case being the same as those of oakwoods, that is, primrose, bluebell and wood anemone—or by internal adaptations in the plant itself, for example the bird's nest orchid *Neottia nidus-avis* is able to grow in deep shade since it does not manufacture its own food.

The following plants are among those typical of beechwoods in southern England although all are not necessarily restricted to this habitat: green hellebore *Helleborus viridis*, uncommon; stinking hellebore *H. foetidus*, uncommon; columbine *Aquilegia vulgaris*, uncommon; wood sorrel *Oxalis acetosella*; bird's nest *Monotropa hypophegea*, uncommon; bird's nest orchid *Neottia nidus-avis*, uncommon; white helleborine *Cephalanthera damasonium* and sword-leaved helleborine *C. longifolia*; common twayblade *Listera ovata*; and fly orchid *Ophrys muscifera*, local.

In open beechwoods a more varied flora occurs containing many of the oakwood species.

Shrub layer. The shrub layer is sparse. Privet *Ligustrum vulgare* and spindle *Euonymus europaeus* are characteristic of the more open parts of beechwoods on the chalk. The spurge laurel *Daphne laureola* and box *Buxus sempervirens* occur locally. It has been suggested that the village of Box in Wiltshire derived its name from the presence of this shrub in the neighbourhood. Holly *Ilex aquifolium* and yew *Taxus baccata* are trees often found in a secondary layer under beech.

Fauna. Various species of Mollusca inhabiting beechwoods include the snail *Helicodonta obvoluta* and a large dark coloured slug *Limax cinereo-niger*.

A certain number of moths are especially associated with beech. The scientific name of the lobster moth *Stauropus fagi* indicates such a connection. The English name derives from the strangely shaped caterpillar which feeds on beech leaves. It is widespread but by no means common in southern England and in addition to the New Forest, which is one of its strongholds, the Berkshire woods are good localities. These Berkshire woods also have the square-spotted clay *Amathes stigmatica*, the reddish light arches *Apamea sublustris* and the beech-green carpet

Colostygia olivata. The clay triple-lines *Cosymbia linearia* and barred hook-tip *Drepana cultraria* are widely distributed.

Many of the birds of oakwoods are also present in beechwoods but the willow warbler is largely replaced by the wood warbler, the bird which attracted Gilbert White's attention as it uttered its sibilant trill from Selborne Hanger and which in 1768 he identified as a separate species in its own right. It is the least common of the three leaf warblers and, although a ground nester, sings and feeds at a higher level than the other two species. An irregular winter visitor to the beechwoods is the brambling, which feeds on the mast. It comes sometimes in large flocks and may join the mixed flocks of finches which haunt the stubble fields.

Ashwoods

Ash is a widespread and important constituent of oakwoods throughout the region, particularly on calcareous soils; but on the Carboniferous Limestone of the Mendips and in the district around Bath it is the dominant species, forming ashwoods.

The ground layer has a varied collection of mosses including *Camptothecium sericeum*, *Ditrichum flexicaule*, the conspicuous *Neckera crispa* and the glossy clumps of *N. complanata.*

There is a rich and interesting flora including the dominant dog's mercury, herb paris *Paris quadrifolia*, the two hellebores, lily of the valley, large white helleborine, madder *Rubia peregrina*, ramsons *Allium ursinium* and the meadow saffron *Colchicum autumnale.* A rare and beautiful flower which is characteristic of the outskirts of Mendip ashwoods is the blue gromwell *Lithospermum purpurocaeruleum.* Woods in the vicinity of Bath have two rare plants which there grow commonly: the early spring-flowering yellow star of Bethlehem *Gagea lutea* and the June-flowering spiked star of Bethlehem *Ornithogalum pyrenaicum.* The young shoots of the last-named were sold for food until recently in Bath shops as Bath asparagus. They are probably still eaten by local people.

A plant bug of northern mountain distribution, *Calocoris major*, is found on nettles in the Mendip woods.

In addition to the more common warblers these woods have tree pipits, wood warblers and, in some places, redstarts.

Since birch is not climax vegetation but develops as a secondary stage of succession on heaths, the birchwood communities will be dealt with in the chapter on heathland.

Coniferous plantations

The Forestry Commission plantations do have a distinctive if limited fauna of their own. The pattern of the wild life in fact changes with the various growth stages of the trees. If the ground previously carried an oakwood a thick ground cover of bramble, bracken and other plants of deciduous woods continues to flourish for the first few years. Where the planting has been made on heathland the bird life includes such species as stonechats and grasshopper warblers. The latter appear in recent years to have extended their range from marshy habitats by colonising these young plantations. Provided there are a few isolated trees such as birches left standing on the heath, tree pipits find these plantations ideal nesting terrain.

Gradually the closely planted seedlings by their growth and shade smother the field layer as they reach what the forester terms the thicket stage. The birds are unable to tolerate the changed conditions and leave. This stage is the most barren of all for plant and animal life. Sparse societies of bracken grow on the outskirts and stretch tenuous arms under the trees but under the dense cover nothing can grow.

Brashing, that is removal of the lower branches, signals the commencement of the pole crop stage during which progressive thinning takes place. Goldcrests and tits, particularly long-tailed and coal tits, forage through the tree tops although some decaying timber is necessary for the nesting of most species. The ubiquitous robin, blackbird and wren are present and as the canopy is opened more species can establish themselves.

Mature plantations with tall well-spaced conifers will have chaffinches, thrushes, wood pigeons and woodpeckers. Tree creepers are unobtrusive but common, and they have developed the habit of roosting in the bark of wellingtonias as at Ashton Park near Bristol. The magnificent avenue of sequoias at Finchampstead in Berkshire would be worth inspecting for such roosts. Where there are clearings some of the summer warblers set up their territories. The long-eared owl is a very scarce breeder in coniferous plantations. It is an unusually silent bird, normally calling only for a short period in the early spring, and this coupled with its nocturnal nature may mean that it is frequently overlooked, for records over the years come in sporadically from widely scattered localities. It is not now known to breed in Somerset or the Isle of Purbeck; it has bred and may still breed on the Marlborough Downs, the Cranborne Chase area of north Dorset and a few places in Hampshire, but much needs to be discovered about its status in the region.

There are a number of insects typical of mature conifers. The pine hawk *Hyloicus pinastri* is a large moth which can be seen in daytime resting on the trunk of mature Scots pine. The species only began spreading in southern England after about 1930, previous to that it was mainly restricted to East Anglia. It became established in Dorset and in 1945 began moving eastwards into Hampshire where it is now fairly common. The northward spread into Wiltshire came a little later but it is now widespread in suitable habitats within the region. The lovely pine beauty *Panolis flammea* is also fairly common, and the bordered white *Bupalus piniaria* a common day-flying moth. In the carpet moths the grey pine carpet *Thera obeliscata* is frequent but the pine carpet *T. firmata* and the grey spruce carpet *T. variata* are much more local species occurring on their respective trees.

Often when a section is felled a certain number of trees are left standing as 'mothers' so that another and self-sown crop of trees may result. The plantation has come full circle and with the increased light, flowers, shrubs and birds once again invade the area. There is, however, one significant difference and that is the presence of these mature standing pines well separated from each other. Such a situation is beloved by crossbills and in those favourable seasons when irruptions occur these are the habitats they seek. Outside the New Forest they are found fairly regularly in the woods at Stourhead.

Deer

Of the six species of deer living in the wild in Britain, five are found within the region and the sixth, the Chinese water deer, did live for a time in a feral state in northern Hampshire. Deer generally are increasing in numbers and spreading in southern England and since some are wanderers may sometimes be seen in places where they have not previously been recorded.

Red deer roam the Quantocks and the New Forest and have done so for hundreds of years, about 300 of them live in the Quantock combes. In the New Forest there are two small herds, one in the north and the other in the south. There are red deer in Savernake Forest, a few in Bramshill Forest, one hind in Harewood Forest and a stag at Porton, Wiltshire, where it grazes with a herd of cows. Occasional wanderers occur in other places in the region from time to time. They have been reported from the Mendips, Dorset and Berkshire as isolated individuals and in 1965 two red stags appeared in a wood at Cheriton, Hampshire, subsequently wandering together over a large part of southern Hampshire until one of them met with a fatal accident.

Fallow are more numerous and widespread. There are relatively few in Somerset in southern localities indicated on the map (see opposite) and in Selwood Forest in the east, but as we have seen this is not a well-wooded county. They are fairly common in the other four counties, and form the most common species in the New Forest where most are of the variety which changes its coat in winter but there are a few white specimens and one or two with black pelage.

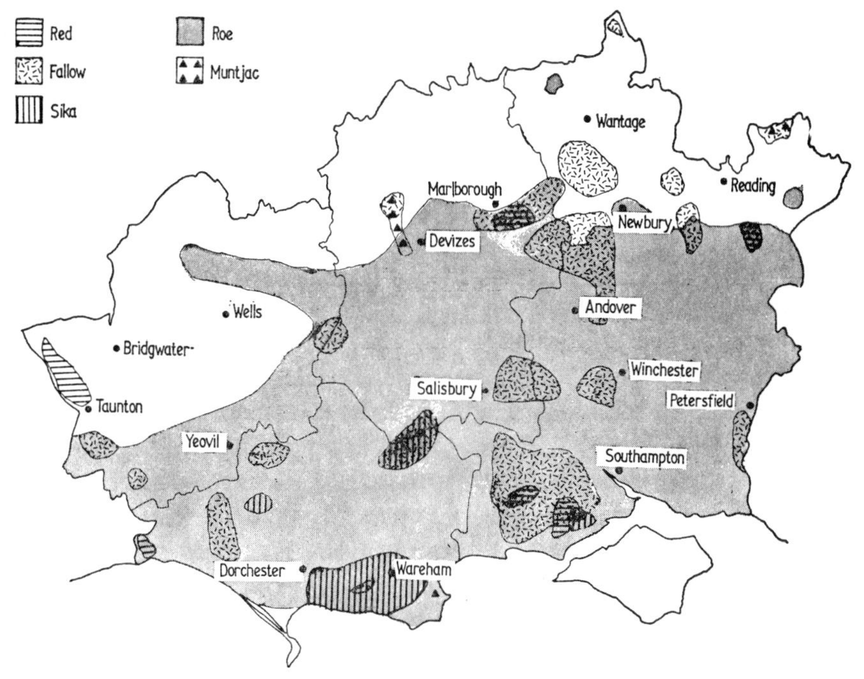

Map showing distribution of deer in the region. Based upon the Ordnance Survey Map with the sanction of the Controller of HM Stationery Office, Crown copyright reserved. Roe deer are found in suitable habitats within the shaded zone. Individual red deer occur in a few additional localities

Each species of deer has its own interesting features. The Japanese sika must be noted for the astonishing and stirring whistle of the stag during the autumn rut in contrast to the barks and bellowing of other deer. A sika herd lives in the southern part of the New Forest, in the woods around Beaulieu, and another in Cranborne Chase, but the biggest concentration within the region, and incidentally the largest in this country, is in the Wareham–Isle of Purbeck area. They have originated from two sources. Stock was put down on Brownsea Island in 1896. Some soon swam ashore to the woods on the western side of the harbour at Rempstone but a number lived on Brownsea until World War II. The second source was from park deer kept at

Hyde Park near Wareham from 1900 onwards. These began escaping in 1926 and the entire herd left the park during World War II. Their habitat preference is for thick plantation especially with bog or salt marsh in the vicinity. The Poole Harbour basin is thus ideal for them and although they are not wanderers as some other species they have slowly increased and spread westwards almost to Dorchester.

Roe deer are small, very graceful creatures and the buck in his summer coat of fox-brown is one of the most handsome of woodland animals. Their preferred habitat is a young conifer plantation before and during the thicket stage as dense cover for lying up is essential. The great increase in coniferous afforestation in recent years has resulted in a corresponding increase in the roe population. The bucks do considerable damage by fraying young trees. In contrast to sika they are great wanderers and adept at colonising new plantations.

They are particularly common and well-distributed in Hampshire, Wiltshire and Dorset. In Berkshire they are only well established in the south-west of the county and Somerset is as yet not well populated. They occur, for example, at Castle Neroche Forest in the south and on the Mendips in the north, but not on the Quantocks although there is much suitable terrain. Whilst white fallow are not all that unusual, white roe are very rare; since 1965 a small wood in western Dorset has had a roe doe with a white head and neck. Much still remains to be discovered about roe deer behaviour and studies are currently being carried out by the Forestry Commission.

Muntjac are the last species to be considered. They are much the rarest of the five species and have spread into the region from Bedfordshire, where they were introduced in the last century. In the 1950s a southward movement began from the Chilterns, and by 1956 the Thames had been crossed and the region entered, for in this year a buck was seen and shot in a garden in Twyford, Berkshire. A colony is now established in the woodland centred on Ashley Hill in the loop of the Thames between Reading and Maidenhead.

The presence of muntjac in Dorset was confirmed in 1962, when one was shot at Melbury Osmond. Since then a small number have lived in a coastal village in south Dorset on a piece of waste ground with bramble thickets backed by a small sallow and hawthorn wood. Here in the evenings, with supreme disregard for the forces of law and order, they feed in the local policeman's garden.

Elsewhere one or two are found in the border country where Hampshire, Wiltshire and Dorset meet. Their presence in Wiltshire was not confirmed until 1967, when they were reported from the northern part of the county near Devizes and Chippenham, having presumably spread south from the Cotswolds. It is possible that they may have spread to a few woods in north Somerset, for they are even greater travellers than roe and can easily be overlooked.

CHAPTER SIX

Heaths and commons

Plants–Invertebrates–Reptiles–Birds–Birchwoods

'COMMON LAND' IN its technical use means land over which certain people have common rights; it includes a variety of habitat such as meadows, downland, beaches and village greens, and contrary to popular belief does not necessarily mean that the public has a right of access. In this chapter the word is used in a much more limited sense, to refer to open land with scrub growth either bearing a similar flora to heathland or, if grazed by cattle, having a grass heath community.

The heaths of southern England are usually sited in exposed lowland situations on shallow acid soils of sand or gravel. The natural succession if left undisturbed is through birch and pine to oak climax woodland. Birch is plentiful but a number of factors such as grazing and burning prevent the heaths from developing into oak forest.

The habitat is a rapidly disappearing one. Outside the New Forest the largest areas are found in a fragmentary group of heaths in eastern Dorset. Originally one vast area they have dwindled in 150 years from 75,000 to 25,000 acres. They, and others in the region, have been appropriated for a number of different uses. Some have been reclaimed for agriculture and forestry; some have suffered development, the city of Poole, for example, was built on heathland; some have had golf courses constructed on them, whilst the insatiable demand for houses has meant a great increase in the number of gravel pits, although these usually create only a temporary disturbance and the land can in some cases revert to its former state. The great inroads into heathland during this century, however, if continued at the current rate will mean that soon there will be no heaths left except those which have been saved by National Trust ownership or by being declared nature reserves.

Hampshire has by far the largest area of common land with some 16,000 acres although some of this acreage will not come within the scope of this chapter for the reasons set out in the first paragraph of this chapter. South-western Hampshire not only has the vast heather tracts of the New Forest but also heaths flanking the valley of the Avon, chiefly on Valley Gravel. East of Southampton there are some relatively small areas of common land, but the northern part of the county is better endowed with open land such as Yateley Common, Hazeley Heath and Heckfield Heath although this last is now largely woodland. In the east of the county some areas of common land are in military occupation around Aldershot and Woolmer Forest, but the National Trust owns Passfield Common and Conford Bog.

In Berkshire there are heathy commons on Plateau Gravels south of Newbury, a line of heaths north of Newbury parts of which are scheduled as Sites of Special Scientific Interest, and fragmentary heath in the Crowthorne area although most of this is now wooded or built on. Dorset has an expanse of heather on Blackdown Hill south-west of Dorchester and various commons in the north and west, as well as the great heaths of the Poole basin. Wiltshire has only a small area of heathland in the south-east at Landford and a few commons near Shaftesbury, and in Somerset sandy heathland is rare except on the Quantocks and Mendips, though the county is well-furnished with commons.

Plants

There is a paucity of flowering plants on heathland. The soil is often acid and deficient in nutrients, the surface minerals having been deposited at a lower level by a process known as leaching. This process whitens the sand and is a feature which can frequently be seen along exposed tracks. Iron carried down from the surface often forms an impervious layer known as iron pan.

The principal plant community is dominated by ling *Calluna vulgaris*. In places this is almost a pure consociation except for the lichens *Claydonia* spp, their little red fruiting tubercles making attractive dots of colour under the heather, and various grasses, notably *Molinia coerulea* in the wetter parts and *Agrostis setacea* in the dry, although the last-named is of only local occurrence in Berkshire. Ling is often associated with other ericaceous plants. Wetter ground brings in the cross-leaved heath *Erica tetralix* whilst on really dry soil, as for example on a sandy bank, bell heather *E. cinerea* replaces ling. On some of the dry heaths bilberry *Vaccinium myrtillus* is locally distributed. On many heaths there are areas of bracken *Pteridium aquilinum* but ling and bracken have an uneasy relationship and where one or other of the species is dominant it virtually excludes the other. Characteristic, often abundant, small flowers are the heath milkwort *Polygala serpyllifolia*, heath lousewort *Pedicularis sylvatica*, tormentil *Potentilla erecta*, heath bedstraw *Galium saxatile* and devil's bit scabious *Succisa pratensis*. A parasitic plant on heather is the lesser dodder *Cuscuta epithymum*.

The common gorse *Ulex europaeus* is widespread and locally abundant although not able to compete with the ling consociation. It grows particularly well on disturbed soil and the frequency of its occurrence on roadsides verges is a noticeable feature of the region. There are two smaller species of gorse often mistaken by the public for young plants of common gorse. The dwarf gorse *U. minor* is a plant of south-eastern distribution and is locally frequent in Hampshire, Berkshire, south-east Wiltshire and eastern Dorset. In western Dorset and Somerset it is replaced by the western gorse *U. gallii*. In places this is locally dominant as at Lambert's Hill Common on the Devon–Dorset boundary, where it grows in association with purple moor grass. Western gorse does occur as far east as the extreme south-west corner of Hampshire but it is not known in Berkshire. A few fungi grow on gorse stems, notably *Collybia velutipes* and, after heath fires, the small circular fungus *Daldinia concentrica*. Another member of the gorse family *Genistae anglica*, known as petty whin, is well distributed. Broom *Sarothamnus scoparius* is locally plentiful. An uncommon heather of distinction is the Dorset heath *E. ciliaris* which within the region is found on the Purbeck heaths. It is most abundant on Hartland Moor, the National Nature Reserve. Outside of the region it is only known from a few localities in Devon.

As in the New Forest, boggy hollows occur on some of the heaths. Shrubs such as dwarf sallow *Salix repens* and bog myrtle *Myrica gale* are frequent and the plants of this habitat will be described in the chapter on the New Forest.

Invertebrates

The common grasshopper of the driest parts of the heaths is *Myrmeleotettix maculatus* with varied and mottled coloration: the species is darker in colour when seen on young heather growing on soil blackened after a fire. The meadow grasshopper *Chorthippus parallelus* is frequent in the rather moister areas. Amongst bog myrtle may be found the bog bush cricket *Metrioptera brachyptera* whilst the great marsh grasshopper *Stethophyma grossum* is frequent on the Dorset heaths generally and not confined to the wettest patches. The dry parts of these Purbeck heaths are the principal British locality for the heath grasshopper *Chorthippus vagans* which is plentiful in some seasons. This species was first identified as occurring in Britain when one was caught near Studland in 1933. The very rare wart-biter *Decticus verrucivorus* is confined within the region to one heath in eastern Dorset.

Among the butterflies, the silver-studded blue *Plebejus argus* and the grayling *Eumenis semele* are especially typical of this habitat, the colour of the latter merging perfectly with the sandy or gravelly ground on which it loves to rest. The former insect is locally common and sometimes abundant on the heaths of Dorset, Hampshire and Berkshire but very scarce in Wiltshire and Somerset, two counties with little heathland. Brown argus

Aricia agestis, Duke of Burgundy fritillary *Hamearis lucina*, marbled white *Melanargia galathea*, green-veined white *Pieris napi* and several of the skippers are fairly frequent on commons.

Many kinds of moth inhabit heathland, the following being characteristic species: emperor *Saturnia pavonia*, fox *Macrothylacia rubi*, common heath *Ematurga atomaria*, heath rustic *Amathes agathina* and beautiful yellow underwing *Anarta myrtilla*.

Gorse is the food plant of the caterpillars of the lead belle *Ortholitha mucronata*, as broom is of the broom-tip *Chesias rufata*. The caterpillars of the mottled grey *Colostygia multistrigaria* feed on bedstraw; it is a rather local species in the region but a large colony is recorded from Heckfield Heath in north Hampshire. Ling, the food plant of many insects, also feeds such local species of moth as the horse chestnut *Pachynemia hippocastanaria* and the bordered grey *Selidosema plumaria*. The purple moor grass is the food of the marbled white-spot larvae *Jaspidia pygarga*, locally common in the region. The bogs of the Purbeck and Hampshire heaths are the only British localities of a small plume moth *Stenoptilia pneumonanthe*, its larvae feeding on the seeds of marsh gentian. Another local micromoth of these bogs is *Trichoptilus paludum*, the larvae feeding on sundew.

Hymenopterons of many species are abundant on the dry sandy ground. Probing deeply into the heather bells or buzzing noisily on their way, the cumbersome bumble-bees are seen in the summer. The small earth bumble-bee *Bombus lucorum* is one of the commonest, perhaps more so than its larger relative the large earth bumble-bee *B. terrestis*. The heath bumble-bee *B. jonellus* and the common carder *B. agrorum* are widely distributed and a number of others occur. Solitary bees and wasps are plentiful: distinctive ones include the heath potter wasp *Eumenes coarctata*, whose little earthen cells are occasionally to be seen on the stems of heather, and the very common sand wasps *Ammophilia* spp, which with their elongated abdomens are a familiar sight on bare sandy ground. The typical ants of heathland will be described in the New Forest chapter. Morden Bog

Page 143 (*above*) Marsh gentian on the left, growing in its New Forest habitat amongst bog myrtle and cross-leaved heath; (*below*) historic photograph of the great fall at Gore Cliff, Isle of Wight on 26 July 1928 when about 200,000 tons collapsed on the roadway in right foreground

Page 144 (*above*) Newtown Marsh, Isle of Wight, a local nature reserve; (*below*) marsh mallow on the Newtown reserve

in Dorset has a colony of the rare hairy wood ant *Formica nigricans* as well as *F. picea.*

Various beetles can be seen on the dry sandy soil. The devil's coach horse *Staphylinus olens* wanders across the pathways and if alarmed it will raise its abdomen vertically as though attempting to stand on its head. The tiger beetle *Cicindela campestris* is typical of this habitat. On the Dorset Blackdowns not long ago I spent an interesting half hour watching a tiger beetle larva appearing and disappearing at his burrow entrance like a clockwork toy. Perhaps the *Geotrupes* beetles are the ones most likely to be seen, as they blunder their way across the paths. A close relative is *Typhaeus typhoeus* which lays its eggs in rabbit dung. The uncommon and beautiful ground beetle of bogs, *Carabus nitens,* occurs on some boggy heaths. A number of weevils feed on gorse, two of the commonest being *Apion ulicis* and *A. striatum.* The heather weevil *Strophosomus sus* is often abundant in ling. Some years ago plague proportions of this insect occurred at Ringwood Forest damaging plantations of Corsican pine.

Plant bugs associated with ling include the heath damsel bug *Nabis ericetorum, Orthotylus ericetorum* and an uncommon species *Nysius helveticus,* which in the region is known only from Hampshire and Dorset. Well distributed on gorse are the gorse shield-bug *Piezodorus lituratus* and the gorse lacebug *Dictyonota strichnocera.* Bracken has the bracken-bug *Monalocoris filicis* and broom is the food of several species of *Orthotylus.* Heath bedstraw and lady's bedstraw have the bug *Lignotes picipes.* It is remarkable that so many insects of this order are specific to one plant or at least to one plant family. In other orders only the weevils and leaf beetles can be compared with them in this respect.

Very conspicuous in the summer are the tunnel webs of the spider *Agelena labyrinthica.* The wolf spiders *Lycosa* spp can often be seen hunting their prey, and belonging to this family but of a different genus is the very rare *Tarentula fabrilis,* which is found in a few Dorset localities. In the heather, common spiders include

Agroeca proxima, *Epeira adianta* and *Peponocranium ludicrum*. The rare *Uloborus walchenaerius*, the spinner of a horizontal web on ling, is found in the New Forest and also in a few places in Dorset. One of the crab spiders frequently found on gorse is *Xysticus audax*. In June 1971 in Morden Bog, Dorset, an interesting discovery was made by Dr P. Merrett of the Nature Conservancy: this was the spider *Altella lucida* which is 1mm in length; the only other British record of this extremely rare species is of one found at a house in Hoddesdon, Hertfordshire, in 1880.

Reptiles

Vipers are widespread on dry heathland and black and red varieties occur. Grass snakes are plentiful on commons and the wetter parts of heaths. The rare smooth snake is found on the Dorset heaths as well as in the New Forest. It used to occur in the Bagshot Sand area of south-eastern Berkshire but has not been recorded there in recent years. The common lizard is well distributed on commons and heaths but its rarer relative the sand lizard is almost entirely confined in the region to the Dorset heaths and the western parts of the New Forest although it is recorded occasionally from north-eastern Hampshire and from Windsor Great Park. An attempt is being made by the Dorset Naturalists' Trust with the co-operation of the Forestry Commission to improve conditions for sand lizards by maintaining in Wareham Forest an area of sand quite devoid of plant cover, as this is essential for breeding purposes. Here, at the end of June, the female excavates a hole in loose sandy soil and deposits her eggs several inches below the ground surface.

Birds

Common birds in dry heathland are few in number, the meadow pipit in ling, linnet and stonechat in gorse and the wandering cuckoo echoing above. But certain birds of other habitats regularly feed there, the boggy parts bring in additional species and finally there are a number of more local species.

Where there is adjacent woodland birds such as carrion crow, kestrel and buzzard frequently feed on the heath. The woodland fringe and tree clumps are favoured haunts of woodcock, nightjar, tree pipit and wood lark. Of these the nightjar is rather scarce and the wood lark has decreased alarmingly. Rough scrub growth on commons and heaths are the haunt of red-backed shrikes but these, too, have become exceedingly scarce in recent years. Their status in Somerset is very precarious though a pair or so may still nest in the north-west; they are rare in Wiltshire, and in Purbeck, where one would certainly expect to find the red-backed shrike, it has not been known to breed since 1955. Probably the New Forest is still its main stronghold within the region though even here it has declined greatly. Its larger relative, the great grey shrike, is a scarce but regular winter visitor to commons and heaths. Common whitethroats and yellowhammers are fairly frequent in gorse and in the shrub layer on commons and heaths although the yellowhammer is a somewhat local bird in Somerset.

On the low-lying parts of some heaths and on some of the Somerset commons curlews breed. The montagu's harrier is a bird of prey which nested fairly regularly on the wetter parts of southern heaths up to recent years but although individuals are seen during the summer in most years in Dorset and Hampshire, increasing human pressure is likely to prevent breeding again.

Whinchats are locally common summer visitors in Somerset, but elsewhere they are only sporadic occasional nesters except in the New Forest and one or two Berkshire localities. The main haunts of the dartford warbler are now the Purbeck heaths, where at Arne the Royal Society for the Protection of Birds have established a reserve for them. It has been estimated (Tubbs 1967) that the total population of this beautiful warbler in England in 1961 may have been about 450 pairs. Well over 75 per cent of these occurred within the region, principally in the New Forest. The severe winter of 1962–3 had a disastrous effect and the total population within the region in 1963 may have been less than a dozen pairs. Recovery has been faster on the

Dorset heaths than in the New Forest where there were some six pairs in 1966 and only ten known pairs by 1970.

Birchwoods

Birch trees are found forming small woods; they also grow as virtually a weed crop in conifer plantations. Their true place in natural succession, however, is on heathland as the first of the tree colonisers.

There are a number of fungi particularly associated with birch. On Southampton Common where birches are numerous the brilliant fly agaric *Amanita muscaria* is plentiful. Other fungi growing on the ground under birch are *Lactarius turpis, L. vietus, Russula versicolor* and *Cortinarius pholideus.* Frequent on the trunks are the birch polyphores *Grifola sulphurea* and *Lenzites betulina.*

Typical moths are: birch mocha *Cosymbia pendularia,* argent and sable *Eulype hastata,* silvery arches *Polia tincta,* yellow horned *Achyla flavicornis,* orange underwing *Brephos parthenias,* scarce prominent *Odontosia carmelita,* and grey birch *Ectropis punctulata.*

Common plant bugs include the birch shield-bug *Elamostethus interstinctus* and the parent-bug *Elasmucha grisea,* the female of which has the habit unusual in insects of caring for the young larvae.

CHAPTER SEVEN

Farmland

Plant life–Invertebrates–Mammals–Birds–Conservation and the farmer

FARMLAND CONSTITUTES THE great bulk of the land surface of the region. To take one county, Somerset, as an example, of a total of 1,032,059 acres no fewer than 795,000 acres are agricultural land, a proportion of three-quarters which is closely paralleled in the other counties.

What was once permanent grass such as downland is more and more coming under the plough; in 1881 grassland in Hampshire comprised 199,100 acres but by 1962 this had declined to 148,700 acres; the situation is more drastic in Wiltshire where 130,000 acres of downland were ploughed in 21 years between 1940 and 1961; the decline sadly continues. The process is less marked in Somerset which is a leading milk producing area and still has five-eighths of agricultural land down to grass. Many of the farms are of small size and more than half of Somerset farms are under 50 acres. Much larger farms are found on the downland: firstly because the boundaries were originally determined by the old wide-ranging sheep walks; secondly because the smaller farms are being amalgamated to form larger economic units.

The type of farming varies from district to district, depending amongst other factors on the nature of soil, climate, proximity to urban populations and traditional customs, although there have been considerable changes in this century and traditions have often been vanquished by economics. If a generalisation had to be made, it could be said that there is mixed arable on the chalk and dairy farming on the clay lowlands, but the picture is more complex than that. There are large areas of cereals, especially barley, on the downs and to a lesser extent on some of the lowlands. Sheep rearing has greatly declined but some are still bred on the downs of north Hampshire, Berkshire, Wiltshire and Dorset, whilst in Somerset some are kept on the Quantocks, principally for store rearing, and in south Somerset, where the Dorset breeds are reared. Wessex Saddleback and Large White pigs are, with poultry, increasing on many farms, especially in Wiltshire and Dorset.

The Tertiary clays and loams of south Hampshire, the clay vales of Dorset and Wiltshire, and in Somerset the Mendips, Blackdown Hills and the Vale of Taunton Deane are largely used for dairy farming although this last is a very fertile valley with a considerable amount of mixed farming as well. In Dorset, Blackmoor Vale which contains the river Stour is thought particularly suitable for beef cattle, and Marshwood Vale, the valley of the river Char, consisting of an anticline of soft Liassic shales, sands and clays, has many small dairy farms which used to produce Dorset Blue Vinney cheese and cider. The 155,000 acres of the central plain of Somerset contains many mixed farms and the land is fertile, especially on the Liassic soils around South Petherton and Martock.

Market gardens are found on an extensive scale near large towns where soils are suitable. On the South Levels near Langport are 2,000 acres of osiers, grown for basket-making, and on the North Levels the production of horticultural peat is a growing industry, having increased from an output of 16,000 tons in 1954 to 63,000 tons twelve years later. The Somerset cider apple orchards are well known and although they have been greatly reduced, the old smaller ones being dug up to the detriment of hole-nesting birds, there are still some 15,000 acres. Orchards are also found in west Dorset and in the Vale of Pewsey in Wiltshire. Watercress is a thriving industry in parts of central and north Hampshire, Dorset and north Wiltshire, and mushrooms are grown in disused railway tunnels in Hampshire and in caves at Bradford-on-Avon.

All this variety produces its own distinctive wild life. The watercress beds have over-wintering green sandpipers and an occasional water pipit; in the old cider-apple orchards redstarts and woodpeckers nest; the osier beds have associated weevils; in the barley fields the triple call of the quail is sometimes heard, and even today some cornfield weeds such as the corn marigold have not been entirely extinguished; the dairy-farm meadows have their quota of skylarks, starlings and lapwings; the soft-fruit crops have their complement of blackbirds and bullfinches and the peat extractions their rich bog flora and fauna.

Plant life

Much grassland in these days is in the form of temporary leys, but old pastures on ill-drained low-lying clays have a highly characteristic flora, including: cuckoo flower *Cardamine pratensis* (an unusual form grows in Marshwood Vale in shady sites), daisy *Bellis perennis*, dandelion *Taraxacum officinale*, green-winged orchis *Orchis morio*, meadow buttercup *Ranunculus acris*, and self-heal *Prunella vulgaris*. The northern fen orchid *Dactylorchis purpurella* with its brilliant magenta colour is a northern species that does not, in the main, occur further south than the Midlands, but there is a surprising outlying colony in a damp meadow in a village on the eastern outskirts of Southampton. A small field in east Dorset has the only station in southern England of *Scorzonera humilis*, a relative of the garden vegetable of that name and of the allied salsify.

On the leguminous grassland of the Lias clays of south Somerset, known locally as 'teart' pastures, there is an excess of the rare element molybdenum which produces an illness in cattle; this excess has to be off-set by applications of copper sulphate to the land.

Where meadows are laid up for hay a rather different flora emerges and taller plants can thrive. Typical plants include: meadow vetchling *Lathyrus pratensis*, pepper saxifrage *Silaum silaus*, great burnet *Sanguisorba officinalis* (locally common in Thames water meadows, uncommon elsewhere), tufted vetch *Viccia cracca*, meadow foxtail *Alopecurus pratensis*, and lesser knapweed *Centaurea nigra*.

Grassland on lighter soil has bulbous buttercup *Ranunculus bulbosus*, ox-eye *Chrysanthemum leucanthemum*, ragwort *Senecio jacobae*, and milfoil *Achillea millefolium*. Ox-eye is eaten by horses and sheep but is reported to be unpalatable to cows. The strenuous efforts to eliminate weeds in cornfields by the application of herbicides has led to a great reduction in their numbers so that flowers which were abundant in the last century are now extremely rare. Nevertheless, some survive. On sandy arable fields, corn marigold *Chrysanthemum segetum*, corn spurrey *Spergula arvensis*, cudweed *Filago germanica*, knawel *Scleranthus annuus*, sheep's sorrel *Rumex acetosella*, small nettle *Urtica urens*, and English catchfly *Silene anglica* (fairly common in south Dorset) are typical.

On heavy soils, field bindweed *Convolvulus arvensis*, redshank *Polygonum persicaria*, coltsfoot *Tussilago farfara*, black nightshade *Solanum nigrum* (increasing but local in Dorset), and common horsetail *Equisetum arvense* are likely.

A great variety of plants is found on calcareous arable land. It is likely that some of these were introduced when Neolithic agriculturalists first began cultivating from the wild grasses. Corn cockle *Agrostemma githago*, is rare, but corn chamomile *Anthemis arvensis*, is locally common. Corn crowfoot *Ranunculus arvensis* is uncommon but fluctuating, corn gromwell *Lithospermum arvense*, is local but common in Wiltshire. The poppy *Papaver rhoeas*, is decreasing, and so is shepherd's needle *Scandix pecten-veneris*.

The ancient strip cultivations of Portland have an abundant coloniser in the sharp-leaved fluellen *Kickxia elatine*, whose late-flowering blooms carpet the ground with splashes of purple and gold. This and its close relative the round-leaved fluellen *K. spuria* are fairly frequent in south Dorset and locally plentiful in other counties on calcareous soils.

Hedgerows and roadside verges are also rich in wild flowers, although not perhaps with the profusion found in some parts of western Britain. Hedge plants must tolerate shade and are represented by such species as garlic mustard *Alliaria petiolata*, hedge mustard *Sisymbrium officinale*, red campion *Silene dioica*, greater stitchwort *Stellarea holostea*, cleavers *Galium aparine*, herb robert *Geranium robertianum* and various vetches and umbellifers. A hedge on the Mendips has an extremely rare sedge, *Carex depauperata*, which rejoices in the descriptive name of starved wood sedge due to the paucity of flowers. This plant is known in only one other locality in Britain. Various climbers such as white and black bryony and old man's beard find ideal support in hedgerows.

The most colourful shrubs in the hedges themselves are found on the chalklands; spindle *Euonymous europaeus*, guelder rose *Viburnum opulus*, wayfaring tree *V. lantana* and dogwood *Thelycrania sanguinea*. The greater the variety of shrubs in a hedge the older it is likely to be; Dr M. Hooper of the Nature Conservancy has postulated the interesting theory that the approximate age of the hedge can be ascertained by the number of species existing in a 30yd stretch of hedgerow, each species representing about 100 years.

A common hedgerow tree is the elm *Ulmus* spp. 1971 will be remembered as the year in which a severe outbreak of Dutch elm disease, a fungal disease carried by bark beetles, took place. Trees died all over southern England, and in the central region Hampshire and the Martock area of Somerset were badly affected; out of 615,000 elms in Hampshire 50,000 had died by the end of the year. As these words are being written there is a report of the appearance of a new and more virulent strain of the disease.

Some of the hedgerow flowers already mentioned colonise the roadsides and conspicuous and colourful plants of road verges include meadow cranesbill *Geranium pratense*, which is common in north Wiltshire and found occasionally elsewhere particularly on heavy soils, chicory *Cichorium intybus*, prickly ox-tongue *Picris echioides* on clay soil, black mullein *Verbascum nigrum* found growing occasionally on calcareous soil, and vervain *Verbena officinalis* a somewhat local plant, decreasing in Berkshire.

There are now many miles of disused railway track throughout the region. When the lines first became disused, the tracksides and cinder beds were quickly invaded by plants from the banks and colonised by species, often annuals, of arid conditions. There is great variety as the following two lists show:

Old GW line at Winchester, Hampshire	*Old GW line near Montacute, Somerset*
black medick *Medicago lupulina*	black medick
pineapple weed *Matricaria matricarioides*	pineapple weed
ground ivy *Glechoma hederacea*	poppy *Papaver rhoeas*
coltsfoot *Tussilago farfara*	stinging nettle *Urtica dioica*
mouse-ear hawkweed *Hieracium pilosella*	bindweed *Calystegia sepium*
hemp agrimony *Eupatorium cannabinum*	hemp agrimony
mignonette *Reseda lutea*	ragwort *Senecio jacobaea*
common St John's wort *Hypericum perforatum*	cleavers *Galium aparine*
rosebay *Chamaenerion angustifolium*	rosebay
common toad flax *Linaria vulgaris*	sow thistle *Sonchus oleraceus*
pale toad flax *Linaria repens*	nipplewort *Lapsana communis*
milfoil *Achillea millefolium*	milfoil
ground elder *Aegopodium podagraria*	yellow meadow vetchling *Lathyrus pratensis*
hedge woundwort *Stachys sylvatica*	persicaria *Polygonum persicaria*
buddleia *Buddleja davidii*	figwort *Scrophularia nodosa*
white campion *Silene alba*	red campion *Silene dioica*

It will be noticed that the duplication in these lists is relatively small. A number of plants typical of this situation are of course not in these particular lists.

Invertebrates

Cultivated land carries an enormous population of creatures beneath the surface, springtails, slugs, worms and the larvae of various beetles.

The common green grasshopper *Omocestus viridulus* and the common field grasshopper *Chorthippus brunneus* are widely distributed in the region. The great green *Tettigonia viridissima* occurs in hedges and gardens of Hampshire and Dorset. The field cricket *Gryllus campestris* is very rare but occurs in dry grassland in south Hampshire and the Isle of Wight. The mole cricket *Gryllotalpa gryllotalpa* has been known to damage root crops in alluvial land near Christchurch, Hampshire. In some heated greenhouses in Somerset lives an alien species, the greenhouse camel cricket *Tachycines asynamorus*. The common cockroach *Blatta orientalis* is well distributed throughout the region.

Old hay meadows have a varied assortment of butterflies, browns, blues and skippers. Damp fields have orange-tip *Euchloe cardamines* and green-veined white *Pieris napi*. The large white *P. brassicae* and small white *P. rapae* are very common in gardens, smallholdings and arable fields. In certain years clouded yellows *Colias crocea* are locally abundant during the autumn in clover and lucerne fields. Chalkhill blues *Lysandra coridon* are sometimes seen in barley fields which have replaced downland, the butterflies remaining in the locality though the habitat has been changed. The uncommon wood white *Leptidea sinapis* is recorded from old orchards in south Somerset. The marbled white *Melanargia galathea* is locally common in rough grass and roadside verges being perhaps most plentiful in north Berkshire. Along roadsides also are found wall *Dira megera*, brimstone *Gonepteryx rhamni* and small copper *Lycaena phlaeas* as well as most of the species already mentioned as occurring in meadows. Blackthorn is the food plant of brown-hairstreak larvae *Thecla betulae*, and elm of the caterpillars of the large tortoiseshell *Nymphalis polychloros*, a very scarce species.

The white ermine moth *Spilosoma lubricipeda*, the cabbage moth *Mamestra brassicae* and the large yellow underwing *Triphaena pronuba* are often common in gardens, where the larvae of the last-named in particular can be a pest. The latticed heath *Chiasmia clathrata*, a day-flying moth, is sometimes abundant in clover fields, especially in Wiltshire. The magpie moth *Abraxas grossulariata* is another common species in gardens and the larvae can be a problem where soft fruits are cultivated, the specific name indicating its association with the gooseberry. The turnip moth *Agrotis segetum* is generally plentiful and the larvae are pests in farm root crops. The shark *Cucullia umbratica* can be frequently seen resting on farm fences in the daytime. The uncommon wormwood moth *C. absinthii* is slowly extending eastwards from the West Country and is appearing in waste places in towns in Hampshire and Berkshire where the caterpillars feed on mugwort.

The Brighton wainscot *Synia musculosa* has appeared in Hampshire and Wiltshire in recent years and is now common, even abundant, in some places in the cornfields of north Hampshire and Wiltshire, where in the daytime it can be seen resting on the ears of corn. In 1968 it was observed at Shipham in Somerset. By 1969 its numbers in Wiltshire were reported to be somewhat diminished probably because the requirements of the caterpillars, which need autumn sown corn so that they can spend the winter inside the stems, are not fully met as spring sowing is on the increase.

Coming now to the Diptera, the presence of the cabbage root, carrot, beet, onion and wheat bulb flies is usually recognised only by the damage done to the crops of farmer and gardener. The notorious leather jackets are the larvae of craneflies and are often abundant. In summer the pats of cow dung in the pastures swarm with the yellow dung fly *Scopeuma stercorarium*. The blue and green blow flies, the common and lesser house flies, the flesh flies and cluster flies are all too numerous in dwellings and farmsteads.

Frequently observed beetles in gardens include the large *Carabus violaceus* and another smaller ground beetle *Pterostichus madidus*. The tiny turnip flea beetle *Phyllotreta nemorum* which is less than 3mm long is sometimes common in gardens and where it occurs it destroys young brassica seedlings, as I have good reason to know. The vivid metallic-green tortoise beetle *Cassida viridis* feeds on garden mint. The larvae of the raspberry beetle

Byturus urbanus feeds on the fruit. The larvae of the skipjack beetles of the genus *Agriotes* are the harmful wireworms which often damage grass and root crops. The small *Apion apricans* is a pest in clover fields. Living in dung are a number of different beetle larvae of which the genera *Onthophagus* and *Aphodius* are characteristic.

Mammals

Although not often seen, the mole is very common throughout the region. In farming circles opinions vary on the utility of this creature—though of course the concept that animals exist for man's acquisitive and mercenary desires is fundamentally wrong. Like many another creature found on the farm, moles do good and ill, as, come to think of it, does the owner of the farm himself. They damage temporary leys, without a doubt, but on the other hand, in reasonable numbers they can do little but good in an ill-drained meadow.

The widely distributed shrews and hedgehogs, like the mole, belong to the order Insectivora and are almost wholly beneficial to the farmer and gardener.

Rats, mice and voles abound in farmyards, hedgerows and fields and cause considerable damage. To the naturalist the most satisfactory control is by natural predators such as stoat and weasel. Both are common on farmland within the region, although possibly the stoat is the commoner, even if the weasel, due to its preference for working hedgerows, is more frequently seen. Before the spread of myxomatosis rabbits were the principal prey of the stoat. Now rabbits are recovering and reappearing in many areas, although periodic outbreaks of the disease still occur. The brown hare is in the same family as the rabbit but differs from it in a number of ways, and except when an epidemic of myxomatosis is sweeping the countryside is less numerous. It is nevertheless fairly common in grassland in all the counties of the region and is probably increasing.

Like the fox, the badger wanders far across farmland but unlike him is almost wholly beneficial to the farmer, except for the infrequent 'rogue'. The ignorance that exists regarding the badger is astonishing and dismaying. Even well-educated farmers may request the services of a pest officer on discovering a badger's sett. Persecution of this delightful, inoffensive mammal continues and badger-baiting as a 'sport' is still carried on in parts of rural Somerset. There is a strong case for the protection of the badger by law.

Birds

The birds of farmland are much the same the country over. Among game birds, pheasants are plentiful and widespread. The common partridge is locally common but not as plentiful as it used to be, although more so than the red-legged partridge. There were only four breeding records of the red-legged in Dorset in 1969 and only two for Wiltshire in 1970, but it is still fairly common on the Berkshire downs and parts of Hampshire. Quail are erratic summer visitors, in some years appearing in quantity, small numbers arriving in most years. A few corncrake pass through on migration, and breeding has been proved in Somerset since World War II; but this is now a rare species. The distribution of the corn bunting has been described in Chapter Four.

The skylark is the most typical small bird of the open fields both pasture and arable. The meadow pipit is misleadingly named, being much more typical of uncultivated land, but it occurs in varying numbers on farmland in winter. Lapwings are fairly common throughout the region; their numbers declined in the 1950s but there has been lately some recovery. Farm mechanisation, however, with earlier grass cutting, is harmful for ground-nesting species such as lapwing and skylark. Large lapwing flocks are seen in winter when golden plover more or less regularly frequent certain favoured areas throughout the region, such as Sowley in south Hampshire, the Wiltshire downland around Old Sarum and the coastal flats of Somerset.

In the Purbeck area and on the Berkshire downs they are scarce and chiefly seen on migration.

The resident wood pigeons feed on the arable fields in summer and their numbers are reinforced by flocks of winter visitors. The barn owl, very useful to the farmer, has for some reason become local and scarce in some areas but appears to be increasing a little in Wiltshire and Somerset and is fairly common in Berkshire. Little owls are fairly well distributed although numbers may have declined in Hampshire where records now come mainly from the southern part. Collared doves appeared in the region in the late 1950s and breeding probably first took place in south Hampshire in 1962 and in Salisbury in 1964. Their partiality for the vicinity of chicken runs and flour mills is well known.

Gulls are regular visitors to farmland outside of the breeding season. Herring and black-headed gulls are common on pastures throughout the region; their flight patterns have been referred to in Chapter Three. Common gulls are the most abundant gull in north Wiltshire and in the Newbury district of Berkshire. They are familiar winter visitors in Hampshire and Dorset, but in Somerset appear to be mainly restricted to hill pastures and are scarcer on the plain. The lesser black-backed gull occurs in much smaller numbers than the others mentioned but there are signs of an increase in parts of Somerset, Wiltshire and Berkshire. Winter visitors in the thrush family are the fieldfares and redwings. Rooks are usually regarded as pests by the agriculturalist although their true status is probably a neutral one, their consumption of grain off-set by the enormous number of injurious invertebrates eaten. Other common Corvids are carrion crows, jackdaws and magpies.

Coming to the smaller birds of the farm, starlings accompany the cattle in the pastures and house sparrows flock in the cornfields. Autumn stubble fields sometimes have enormous mixed flocks of finches which occasionally include small numbers of bramblings. A familiar sight on late afternoons in winter is that of hordes of starlings converging on their roosts. A mammoth roost of between half to one million starlings was recorded near Westwood School, Wiltshire, in 1965. Another bird which roosts communally is the pied wagtail, frequently seen around farm buildings and grassland. In the winter of 1967–8 300 wagtails chose to roost inside two nursery-garden greenhouses near Bath. For some years in the 1960s roosting pied wagtails were a problem in the greenhouses of a nursery at Sway, Hampshire. In 1967 the firm enlisted the help of the British Trust for Ornithology who ringed well over a hundred and took them to Tring in Hertfordshire. Twenty-five of them promptly flew straight back without any difficulty to the greenhouses at Sway, a feat which puts human orienteering very much in the shade.

The wren also appreciates warmth and shelter. After the catastrophic decline of the wren population in the hard winter of 1963 it seems that some alteration of habitat was made. K. Williamson states that wrens were then mainly found in woods and along river banks until expansion began, when they moved first of all to orchards and gardens and then, as the increase continued, to hedgerows, which are the least favoured of their haunts.

Characteristic birds of orchards are goldfinches, bullfinches, chaffinches and tits. Flocks of tree sparrows occur in winter throughout the region but they are scarcer in summer; they breed locally in Berkshire orchards but in Somerset appear to prefer the pollard willows on the moors; in Wiltshire tree sparrows are reported to be declining and they rarely nest in Hampshire and Dorset.

Hedgerows carry the usual population of common small birds such as yellow hammers, greenfinches, common and lesser whitethroats, hedge sparrows, robins, song thrushes and blackbirds.

Three summer migrants associated with dwellings in general as well as farmsteads are the swift, swallow and housemartin. The sand martin is a colonial nester in sandpits, sometimes on a large scale.

A new coloniser which may be expected to follow in the wake of the collared dove is the serin. This small finch is particularly associated with cultivated ground, and for the last hundred years or so has been spreading northwards in Europe. In 1967 the first recorded nesting in Britain took place in one of the coastal counties of this region, and subsequently nesting has occurred in an adjoining county. There seems no reason why the serin should not become as common in southern England as on the continent.

Conservation and the farmer

Some welcome attention has recently been devoted to the problems of reconciling economic food production with the conservation of wild life. Farmers and naturalists usually have very different viewpoints and extremists on either side do not help their own causes. The conference of farmers and naturalists held at Silsoe in Bedfordshire in July 1969 was a landmark in the history of the conservation movement in this country. It was only a start, but it was followed a year later by a similar conference in Dorset based on a study of a farm at Hammoon in the fertile Blackmoor Vale, where the owner Mrs A. Hughes is herself a naturalist as well as a farmer. Considerable interest was aroused, and some more members of the farming community became aware both of the need for conservation and of the practical steps which could be taken to achieve it. Independently of this, the John Spedan Lewis Trust at Leckford in Hampshire are carrying out a study of wild life on two areas of this intensively farmed estate to examine the effects of conservation. A few far-seeing farmers are encouraging wild life by leaving uncultivated pockets in field corners; one such, at Purtington, Somerset, has been rewarded with a wealth of wild life—foxes, badgers, roe deer, nightingales and, in a hazel copse, goldilocks and herb Paris. As I was photographing one of these uncultivated pockets a kestrel hovered overhead and a weasel ran across the track in front of me.

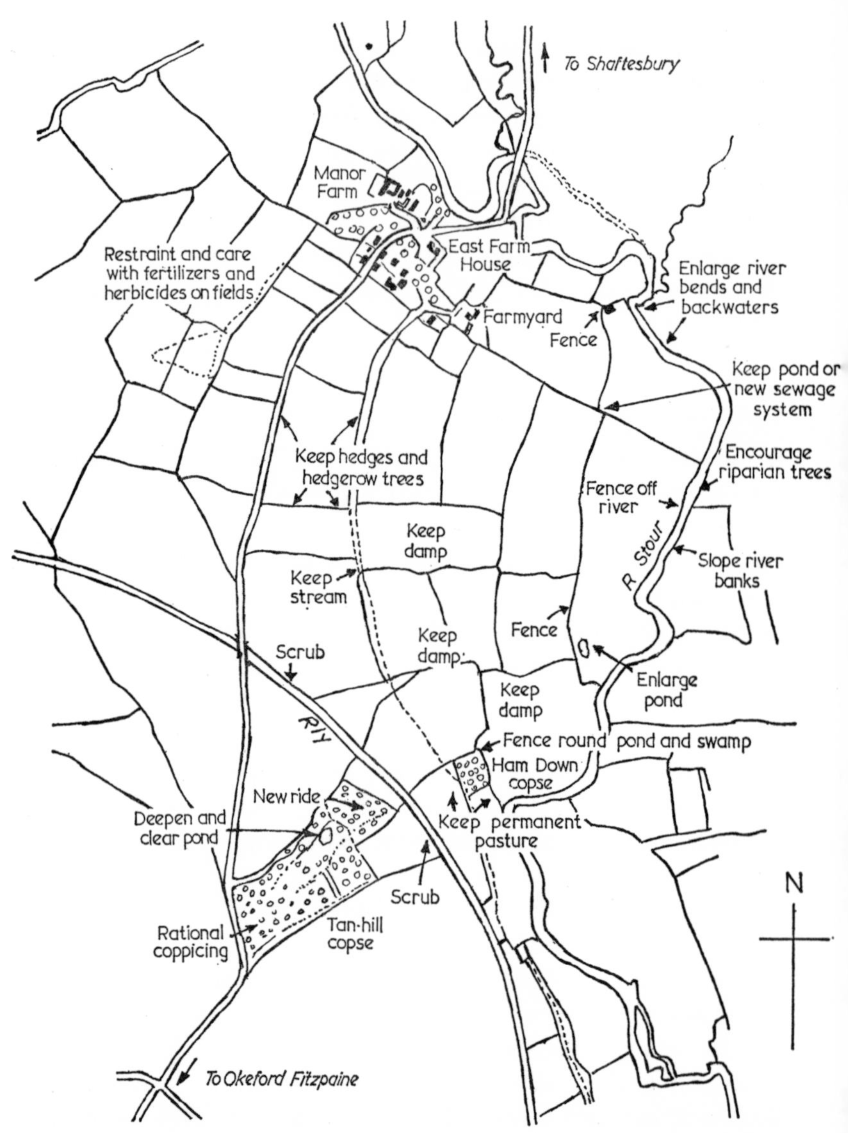

Conservation plan for East Farm, Hammoon, Dorset, showing how farmland can be improved for wild life, from *Farming and Wild Life in Dorset* with permission of Mrs A. Hughes. Based upon the Ordnance Survey Map with the sanction of the Controller of HM Stationery Office, Crown copyright reserved

But alas, the hideous outlawed pole trap is not unknown in the region, although the pressure of public opinion will, it is hoped, do what the law is unable to do by itself.

CHAPTER EIGHT

The New Forest

Geology–Scenery–Streams and ponds–Bogs–Ancient ornamental woods and inclosures–Heathland–Conservation

THE NEW FOREST is an area without parallel in the British Isles. From the savage hunting laws of the Norman kings to the fiercely independent commoners stoutly defending their rights against the Office of Woods in the last century, much has conspired, even if often unwittingly, to preserve it as a mammoth nature reserve. Conservation may be a mid-twentieth century term but in the New Forest it was certainly in existence in 1880 when the Honourable Gerald Lascelles became Deputy-Surveyor. Through the practical interest in wild life of this far-seeing official of the Crown the ancient forest was brought well ahead of its time. What has been achieved, however, has not been without a struggle and nature in the forest today faces as many dangers as in the past.

The New Forest is the home of many rare plants and it is particularly rich in invertebrate life. As a nature lover I have known and loved it; with a countryman's peculiar idea of pleasure I have tramped its woods in winter rain, camped on its heaths on summer nights, endured the ravages of its blood-sucking flies and sunk thigh-deep in its bogs. In this, one of the few remaining wild regions in the South Country, the observer can see wild life in its natural state. Not that man's influence has been insignificant even in this primitive area, but at least here are few of man's dwellings and little of his cultivations.

Geology

All the rocks are sedimentary and all belong to the Tertiary and Quaternary eras although chalk is the underlying rock. As the forest is in the deepest part of the basin no chalk is exposed within the area, the nearest outcrops being the Pepperbox Hill and Dean escarpments in the north and the Isle of Wight downs to the south.

Almost all the London Clay lies outside the forest but a very small area comes just within the boundary at Castle Hill at the western end of Godshill Inclosure. The clay here rests directly on the chalk, and the Reading beds, which would normally intervene, are absent. The next deposit, too, occupies only a small part of the district in the valley bottoms of Ashley Walk. This is the Bagshot Sand. It is a light coloured quartz sand with here and there layers of loam and pipe clay. Sometimes the clays contain impressions of the leaves of deciduous trees.

The Bracklesham beds appear next. In the country east of Southampton these beds produce a good agricultural loam but here they are composed of glauconitic sands and clays. Whilst the Bagshot Sands were deposited by river action these beds are marine. Parts of them contain flint pebbles and fossilised driftwood indicative of the proximity of the shoreline.

Continuing southwards the next deposit encountered is Barton Clay underlying many of the inclosures in the northern part of the forest. This and the succeeding deposit derive their name from the village of Barton on the coast a few miles west of Lymington where the fossiliferous strata are exposed in the sea cliff known to geologists all over the world. Opinions differ on whether Barton Sand should be regarded as forming, with Barton Clay, one deposit, or as a separate bed. It is a layer of very fine sand 60–80ft in thickness deposited on top of the Barton Clay. On the valley sides the junction of the two strata is often marked by swampy ground and the occurrence of springs caused by the rainfall percolating through the porous sand and being held up by the impervious clay. The sand does not contain fossils. Water supplies from this stratum are often discoloured by tannin or iron.

The Oligocene period is of interest in that its rocks in Britain are found only in the New Forest and the northern part of the Isle of Wight. The Headon beds occupy the southern part of the forest and appear on the map as an amorphous patch covering the group of inclosures of which Parkhill, near Lyndhurst, is the centre; they also underlie the Plateau Gravels of the southern heaths. The clays of these beds constitute the best soils for the production of oak.

In Pleistocene times a vast sheet of gravel was deposited, probably by the action of unstable rivers, over much of the New Forest. These beds formed a once continuous sheet but now cap the ridges in the north-west and cover the northern plains. The composition of these gravels is interesting. They contain sub-angular flints, rounded flint pebbles, rare pebbles of quartz and Greensand chert and fragments of shelly limestone. Since part of this material can only have come from the north-west it is clear that it must have been carried by rivers flowing towards what is now Southampton Water. The flint may be presumed to have come from the chalk lands of Salisbury Plain and northern Hampshire. It is suggested that the quartz may have come from Eocene deposits which once overlaid the chalk and the limestone may have come from the vicinity of Shaftesbury. It was during Pleistocene times that the great river Solent, flowing eastwards and entering the sea somewhere off what is now Sussex, was captured by the sea. The present forest rivers were once tributaries of this river.

The land-forms of the forest are geologically of very recent origin. They were moulded within the last million years by the enormous erosions of the Ice Age. The main lines of drainage were already in existence at the beginning of glacial times but the valleys were shallow and the area generally was much more of a southward-sloping plateau than at the present. Each spring vast quantities of melt-water poured southward in a torrent covering the surface with glacial debris. The whole basin was thus covered with what are now termed Plateau Gravels. Subsequent erosion deepened the valleys and removed much of these gravels. With this erosion and the Neolithic land subsidence the forest took its present shape.

Scenery

The best view of the New Forest is the bird's-eye view. From the great central mass of woodland the buzzard rises in a lazy spiral, upward and upward in the clear sky in ever-widening circles with only an occasional flap of outstretched wings, until he becomes a vanishing speck in the blue and then part of the blue itself. We are watching a pin-point of vibrating muscle but the bird in the air has the whole panorama of the forest before its eyes: to the west and just beyond the forest boundary, is the long meandering line of the Avon bordered by lush water meadows; to the east, woods merge into heathland and bog, backed by a low line of cranes and ships' funnels on Southampton Water; to the north, a series of high ridges and deep valleys run south-west to north-east, partially clothed by forest; to the south, a developed area of gardens and houses around Brockenhurst and Boldre is surrounded on each side by extensive heaths, and beyond is a narrow cultivated coastal plain abutting on the Solent. And in the centre, beneath the buzzard's wings, lies a massive core of inclosures; from west to east is a woodland belt that, measured as the ubiquitous crow flies, stretches continuously, apart from two roads and a railway line, for more than nine miles, the living heart of the New Forest.

No reference to the scenery of the forest would be complete without mention of the marked contrasts that each season brings. Springtime here is markedly different from the coppice-with-standards oakwoods of southern England with their sheets of primroses, bluebells and wood anemones. Though of course these plants are found here they do not give their characteristic bold masses of colour, but instead some of the rides are graced by the choice lungwort. The attractions of the woodland at this time are the translucent greens of the beeches and the flight of speckled wood butterflies in the clearings.

Summer brings the humming of myriads of insects. A typical picture that springs to mind is that of a boggy pool, its surface decorated with the white cups of water lilies and above them the scintillating sheen of the blue and green demoiselle dragonflies, while nearby a cuckoo calls.

Perhaps the loveliest season is autumn. On the heaths the ling blooms in purple profusion and the bracken turns russet brown. The woods are decorated with brilliantly coloured fungi, the white-stemmed scarlet-capped fly agaric, the sulphur-yellow polyphore on beech trunks, the beautiful pastel shades of the amethyst *Laccaria laccata* and the purples, browns and reds of the russules. The woods themselves, especially the beechwoods, are a riot of colour.

Autumn gives place to winter and although snow is infrequent the New Forest under snow presents an unforgettable picture. The snow carpet has an added attraction for the naturalist because it discloses the tracks of mammals: deer slot in the rides, the scamperings of voles and field mice under the trees and a badger's foraging.

Streams and ponds

The rivers are essentially moorland and woodland streams, non-calcareous, of moderate current and with gravelly bottoms. Under normal conditions they are shallow, and in the villages water-splashes are a feature. The aquatic plants of a typical forest stream include: water starwort *Callitriche* spp, fool's watercress *Apium nodiflorum*, water crowfoot *Ranunculus aquatilis*, branched bur reed *Sparganium erectum*, flote-grass *Glyceria fluitans*, and water plantain *Alisma plantago-aquatica*.

The beautiful white water-lily *Nymphaea alba* can be found in a number of places in rivers and boggy pools, but the yellow water-lily *Nuphar lutea* is more common. The marsh violet *Viola palustris* is sometimes abundant at stream margins. The great spearwort *Ranunculus lingua* grows in Crockford stream and the red pondweed *Potamogeton alpinus* occurs at Longwater Lawn and one or two other places.

Some of the slower-moving tributaries arise from bogs and sometimes are hardly distinguishable from them; the richness of their plant life compared with that of the faster-flowing main streams is marked. The Rushbush stream is a small tributary of the Beaulieu river. It rises near Dibden Purlieu and traverses one and a half miles of boggy heath before its confluence with the main stream at Ipley. Where it flows through Rushbush Wood the vegetation is naturally sparse but in the open it has a rich flora which include many species indicative of swamp conditions, such as yellow flag *Iris pseudocorus*, watercress *Rorippa nasturtium-aquaticum*, brook lime *Veronica beccabunga*, water mint *Mentha aquatica*, least marshwort *Apium inundatum*, and water dropwort *Oenanthe fistulosa*. Brookweed *Samolus valerandi*, a coastal species, is distributed along the stream banks. In 1951 a comparison of the number of species occurring in sections of the Beaulieu river and Rushbush stream showed that the latter had almost double the number of species and in fact the tributary has an even richer flora in its upper reaches.

The fauna of these streams is markedly less in quantity and in variety of species than that of the chalk streams. H. P. Moon in 1939 found that the average number of insects to a square foot in the Latchmore Brook at Latchmore Bottom was 68 with 10 different species whereas in the Avon it was 380 with 15 species. It is noticeable that in the New Forest streams there is not the density of vegetation, particularly the masses of starwort, which would harbour such a multitude of animal life.

Leeches are prevalent and other Annelids occur. Common Crustaceans include the water louse *Asellus* sp and the freshwater shrimp *Gammarus pulex*. Dragonfly nymphs of running water which are widespread in the forest are those of the demoiselle *Agrion virgo*, the large red damsel fly *Pyrrhosoma nymphula* and the white-legged damsel fly *Platycnemis pennipes*. The banded agrion *A. splendens* prefers streams with muddy, not gravelly, bottoms. Among the darter dragonflies the nymph of the keeled orthetrum *Orthetrum coerulescens* can be found in the deeper parts of some of the streams. Representatives of the large hawker group include the nymph of the golden-ringed dragonfly *Cordulegaster boltonii* which occurs in most streams and the club-tail *Gomphus vulgatissimus* which is found mainly in the Ober water and Avon water.

Stone flies are in all the streams and a number of genera occur. Mayflies are not found in such abundance as in the chalk streams, but there are species, *Baetis rhodani* for example, which are typical of fast-flowing streams. An interesting habit of the females of this genus is their descent through the water to lay their eggs on stones. A local species is *Baetis niger* which has been recorded from the Ober water.

The mayfly nymphs are preyed on by the alder flies *Sialis lutaria* and *S. fuliginosa.* The former is the commoner but both occur in numbers. The larvae of the large Neuropteron *Osmylus fulvicephalus* are very common and the adult is stated to favour the undersides of bridges as resting places.

A few species of water bug frequent running water. There are *Corixa venusta* and *Micronecta poweri* and on the surface, colonies of pond skaters, generally *Gerris najas*, are plentiful in all the streams. Another species is *G. gibbifer* which seems to prefer shallow peaty streams. I have taken this species in a rivulet at spring source at Fritham and it has been reported from a peaty stream near Hasley Inclosure. In the more sheltered parts the water cricket *Velia currens* skates on the surface.

As with water bugs, so with water beetles. Only a small proportion lives in running water. On the surface colonies of the whirligig *Gyrinus natator* are seen in many places. Below the surface *Deronectes depressus* and *D. latus* are fairly common. In the genus *Agabus*, the New Forest contains a very rare species which has been found in only a few places elsewhere in Britain. This is *A. brunneus.* Its normal habitat is shallow, gravelly streams and it lives amongst the stones. The date of its first discovery in the forest is not known but it was certainly before

1855. In 1862 some were discovered near Lyndhurst and since then the species has been found in a number of places. Two beetles can be found fairly commonly in streamside vegetation; these are the distinctively marked *Platambus maculatus* and *Hydraena riparia*. Caddis fly larvae are common in all the streams, both the case-inhabiting and free-living types.

Eels and other small fishes inhabit the streams. On the gravel bottoms stone loaches and bullheads rest motionless waiting for their prey. Generally their mottled scales blend perfectly with the pebbly background but on one occasion I observed a dark coloured bullhead in the Beaulieu river which was very conspicuous against the light coloured gravel. Bullheads also lurk on the fringes of aquatic vegetation bordering open channels where the current carries along small animal life. The brook lamprey is another dweller on the gravel bed feeding on the minute animal life living under the stones. Minnows can be seen in shoals in the open stretches but the three-spined sticklebacks prefer the dense cover of aquatic plants. Ten-spined sticklebacks are much less common but I have caught them in the sluggish Rushbush stream and in the main river at Fulliford Passage. The trout are the dark-coloured type that inhabit woodland streams and appear to be generally quite small in size.

Kingfishers breed but they are not common. Moorhen and mallard nest along some of the quiet stretches.

The ponds are of several different kinds: boggy hollows, flooded gravel pits, bomb craters and mill ponds. Two of the largest are Hatchet and Sowley. The former is bleak and windswept and this is no doubt a contributory factor to the scarcity of flowering plants. There are small societies of broadleaved pondweed *Potamogeton natans*, floating club rush *Scirpus fluitans* and lesser water plantain *Baldellia ranunculoides*. The fish include bream, pike, roach and perch. Mute swans and pied wagtails are the birds of the summer and small numbers of water-fowl visit the pond in winter. Red-throated divers, great-crested grebes, goosanders, wigeon and tufted duck are among those recorded although often only as individuals.

Sowley Pond is 90 acres in extent and has well wooded shores. It probably began as a monastic fish pond and at a later date became the source of power for Sowley Ironworks. Interesting plants here include the frog-bit *Hydrocharis morsus-ranae*, yellow bartsia *Parentucellia viscosa*, lesser reed-mace *Typha angustifolia*, amphibious bistort *Polygonum amphibium* and the rare water-wort *Elatine hexandra*. The New Forest distribution of three species of dragonfly is virtually limited to Sowley: these are the hairy dragonfly *Brachytron pratense*, red-eyed damsel fly *Erythromma najas* and the variable coenagrion *Coenagrion pulchellum*. Common and little terns fish the pond in summer, and winter brings large flocks of duck with occasional small numbers of scaup and smew in cold weather.

In the natural peat pools aquatic plants often include pondweed, but reed, rushes and bladderworts whilst the margins are often fringed with bog St John's wort, marsh pennywort and bog pimpernel.

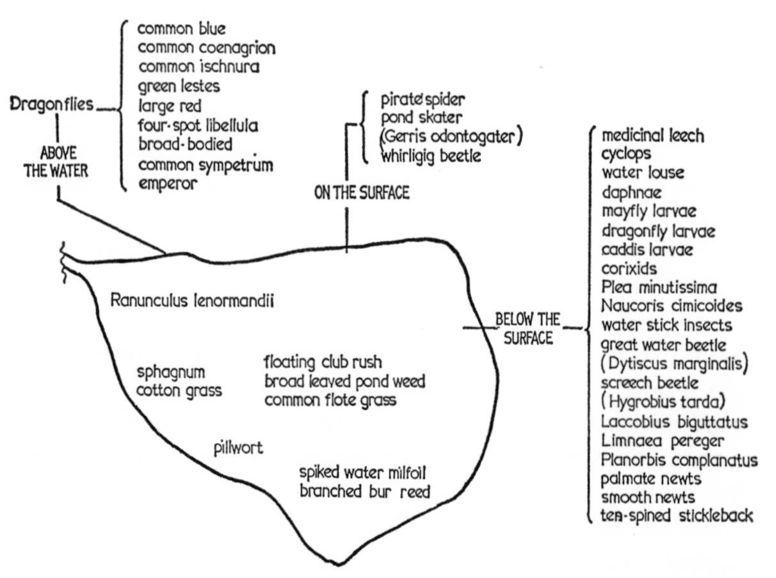

Diagrammatic sketch showing plant and animal life in Furzey Pool, Ipley

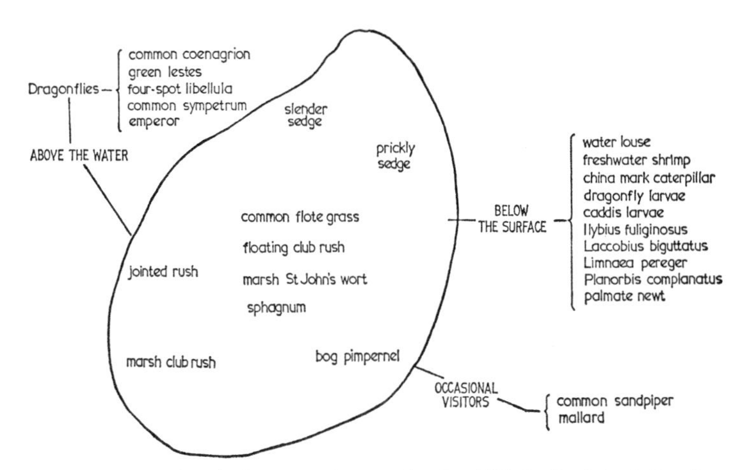

Diagrammatic sketch showing plant and animal life in Rushbush Pond, Ipley

In these boggy pools *Cyclops* and *Daphnae* are often abundant in the mud of the margins. The water louse is more common than the freshwater shrimp. The medicinal leech occurs in some of the pools. Caddis larvae and dragonfly nymphs are plentiful. The great water boatman *Notonecta obliqua* and several species of Corixids abound. A water boatman usually found in brackish water conditions, *N. viridis*, has been taken from a Fritham pond and a rare water bug of the Mediterranean, *Microvelia pygmaea*, has been found in a bog at Bushy Bratley.

Many species of beetle inhabit the ponds. The New Forest may well be one of the most profitable areas in Britain for aquatic coleoptera but the distribution of some species is limited and scattered. This may be due to complex factors in the composition of the pond and to the isolated nature of the habitat. Of the thirty-three species of *Hydroporus* no fewer than twenty-one have been recorded from the New Forest. All of the seven species of *Laccobius* occur and eight of the sixteen species of *Haliplus*. Of the larger beetles, the screech beetle *Hygrobia hermanii* is generally very common. When taken in the hand it frequently stridulates by means of the elytra.

The water spider *Argyroneta aquatica* is plentiful in some of the ponds and is the only spider able to live under water. The common newt in these pools is the palmate; the smooth newt is less common, and the crested newt is certainly the rarest. A colony of the European tree frog has become well established in recent years at a locality in the southern part of the forest. The ten-spined stickleback inhabits a number of the ponds. It is clear that, in the New Forest at any rate, the ten-spined favours stagnant or very slow-flowing water with dense vegetation, whilst the three-spined prefers running water. The surface of these small ponds has its own specialised fauna. The raft spider *Dolomedes fimbriatus* has been recorded from a southern pond. The water gnat *Hydrometra stagnorum* is not as conspicuous as the pond skaters which like the whirligig beetles, occur in colonies.

In summertime, over the water and surrounding bogs, dragonflies hover in abundance. The small red occurs in large colonies and its principal habitat in the forest is the bogs that range along the Ober water. The large red *Pyrrhosoma nymphula*, the common blue *Enallagma cyathigerum* and the common coenagrion *Coenagrion puella* are widely distributed but the southern coenagrion *C. mercuriale* is confined to bogs in the western parts. The scarce ischnura *Ischnura pumilio*, unlike its common relative *I. elegans*, is decidedly uncommon, being confined to certain bogs and not very easily seen. The green lestes *Lestes sponsa* has been recorded from a number of localities but is probably not common. Of the darter dragonflies the broad-bodied libellula *Libellula depressa*, the four-spot libellula *L. quadrimaculata*, the keeled orthetrum *Orthetrum coerulescens* and the common sympetrum *Sympetrum striolatum* are common and widespread. The last named is the commonest dragonfly at Denny Bog in the late summer. The most abundant hawker dragonfly is the southern aeshna *Aeshna cyanea*.

Bogs

The boggy ground is doubtless unattractive to the general public yet, nature study apart, the bogs have their quota of sight, sound and scent to add to the sum total which goes to make up the wild and picturesque New Forest landscape. The vivid emerald green of the sphagnum moss; the white plumes of the cotton grass waving in the breeze; the delicate yellow spires of bog asphodel, all combine to light up the monotone of the enveloping heathland. The air is heavy with the aromatic pungency of bog-myrtle leaves and the luscious heavy scent of water mint, and loud with the calls of curlew.

The bog proper represents the mature development of the bottoms, which are boggy areas in the shallow valleys. There are but few of these well developed bogs, among the largest being Denny and Matley in the south and Wilverley in the north. Nearly all of them are characterised by sluggish streams blanketed with bog-bean, lined by sallow and alder scrub and surrounded by dense vegetation consisting of cotton grass, sedge and numerous other bog plants.

The present bogs must have originated in Neolithic times between 6000 and 3000 BC when there occurred the general land subsidence whose most spectacular result was the severance of Britain from the continent, resulting in the flooding of the river valleys of southern England. In addition, the New Forest streams had worn down to the base level of erosion, being already sluggish in character with stagnant pools. Moreover, the existence of the impermeable strata of Barton Clay and the iron pan in the Barton Sand provided the perfect conditions for bog formation.

So the flat-bottomed valleys became waterlogged and moisture-loving plants multiplied and spread. Quite early in the succession sallow and alder thickets developed along the course of the streams and the irregular lines of these scrub woods are a feature of these bogs. The distinctive conditions of this habitat render it a highly specialised environment for plants and animals peculiarly adapted to living in waterlogged soil.

A number of uncommon plants occur in the bogs. The marsh gentian *Gentiana pneumonanthe* grows in the *Erica tetralix–Myrica*

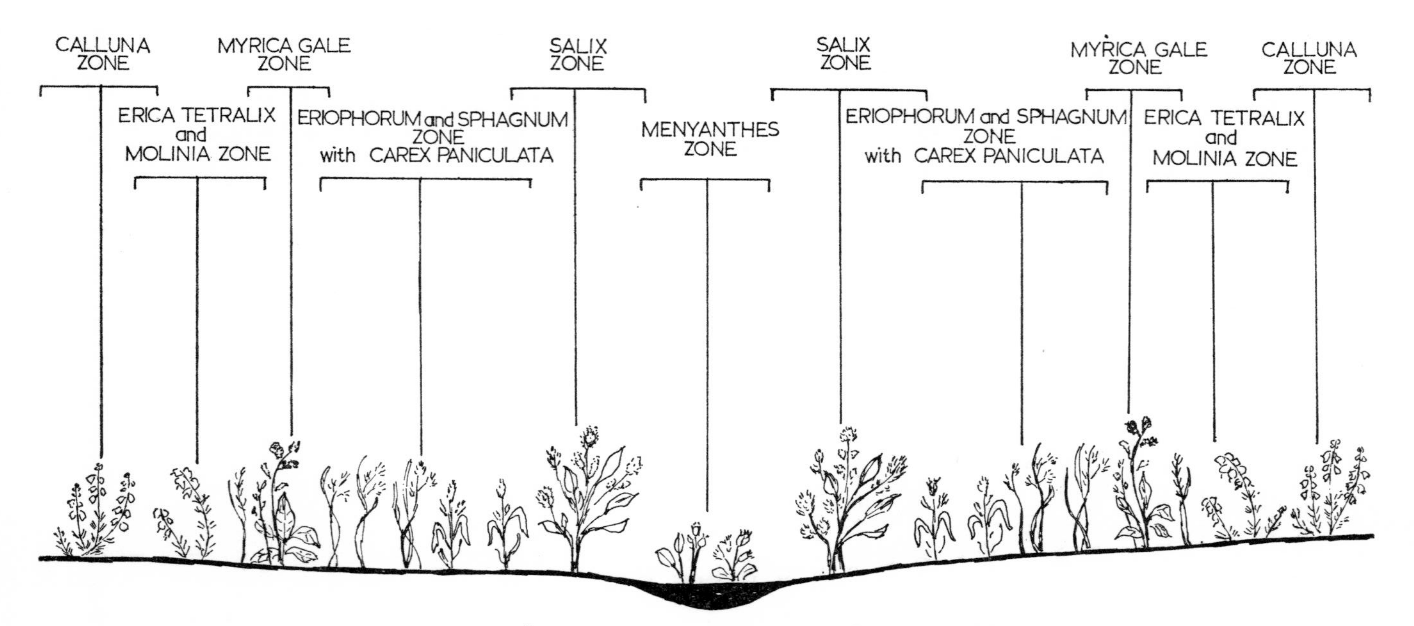

Plant transect across a New Forest bog

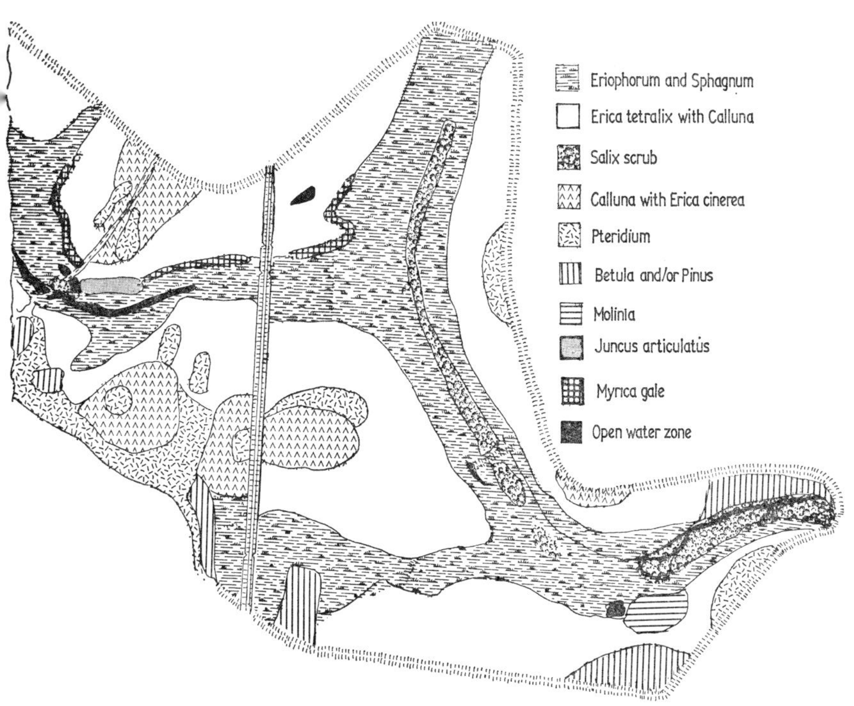

Vegetation map of a part of Denny Bog, New Forest. Based upon the Ordnance Survey Map with the sanction of the Controller of HM Stationery Office, Crown copyright reserved

gale zone. The tiny bog orchid *Hammarbya paludosa* is known from near Hatchet Pond and one or two other localities; it is possible that it occurs in a number of places for it is exceedingly minute and amidst the tall growth of bog vegetation could easily be overlooked. *Cicendia filiformis* is another very small plant found near Hatchet but its habitat is moist heathland rather than bog. The tiny yellow flowers only open in the sunshine. The bladderwort is a curious plant with small bladders formerly thought to be insectivorous but now known to be balancing organs. The lesser bladderwort *Utricularia minor* is found in patches of open water in the bogs and the rarer *U. intermedia* used to occur in Denny Bog but it may have been affected by recent drainage operations.

The common cotton grass is the narrow-leaved *Eriophorum angustifolium* but at least two other species occur. *E. latifolium* has been reported from several places and the very rare *E. gracile* grows on Matley Heath. Holmsley Bog has the mud sedge *Carex limosa* and the great sundew *Drosera anglica.* The forest is one of the few habitats of the small annual, *Ludwigia palustris.* In places on the western part of Beaulieu Heath it luxuriates, covering the ground with a thick blanket of foliage. The rarest of British orchids, the summer ladies' tresses *Spiranthes aestivalis* used to occur in two bogs but it has not been seen for a number of years and must now be regarded as extinct.

A fern which had been feared extinct in the forest due to the fern-collecting mania is the royal fern *Osmunda regalis* but it is still found in a few places. Another uncommon fern, the marsh *Thelypteris palustris*, grows in at least two sallow woods.

Insects make up the great bulk of the wild life population. The marsh bush cricket *Metrioptera brachyptera* is found in the marginal zone of cross-leaved heath and bog myrtle and the great marsh grasshopper *Stethophyma grossus* is found deeper in the bog amongst sphagna.

Seeds of *Juncus* spp are the food of the larvae of a member of the microlepidoptera, the rush moth *Coleophora caespititiella*, and this moth is common where rushes flourish. But the forest abounds in micros and in no habitat are they more in evidence than amongst bog vegetation. As dusk spreads across the wastes, the feeble fluttering wings of many species quicken the rushes and sedges into subdued animation. The larvae of *Cacoecia rosana* feed on bog myrtle and the larvae of *Eulia pulchellana* and *Endothenia oblongana* on marsh gentian flowers. Crambids are particularly abundant. *Eucosma penkleriana* is common amongst alders and distinctive dark forms of *Schoenobius forficellus* have been known at Denny Bog for many years.

There are a few macromoths typical of these bogs. The dingy footman *Eilema griseola* is plentiful amongst the alder swamps. The silver hook *Eustrotia uncula* is a species of eastern England but it occurs in the New Forest. The purple-bordered gold

Sterrha muricata is found on boggy heaths and the small rufous *Coenobia rufa* at Denny Bog and Dibden Bottom.

Very conspicuous are crane flies, the familiar daddy-long-legs, their wings rustling amongst the bog vegetation. A number of rare species of the sub-family Tipulinae are found here. Innumerable mosquitoes, midges and fungus gnats live in this habitat. Of the large Tabanids *Tabanus sudeticus* predominates in the southern bogs whilst *T. bovinus* is more frequent in the northern parts. Several uncommon Tabanids occur including one normally only found in maritime localities.

The moss ant *Leptothorax tuberum* is common in sphagnum moss in the bogs and bottoms. The black bog ant *Formica picae* is a rare species of Matley Bog; the nest of this species, too, is usually in sphagnum. Among the beetles, *Carabus nitens* and *C. arvensis* are found and the rare *Tachys walkerianus* occurs in sphagnum.

The curlew has increased as a breeder and its stirring call is one of the loveliest of sounds in the spring and summer. The tumbling acrobatics of the lapwing in springtime are a joy to watch. The redshank, too, has a brilliant spring display but it is not as common as the curlew or lapwing—and I had almost overlooked the snipe with its wonderful courtship flight which is such a feature of spring. Reed buntings, mallard and sometimes teal, are other breeding birds. One would not perhaps expect to find pheasants nesting in this habitat but several times when stumbling through sedge tussocks I have come upon their nests.

Ancient ornamental woods and inclosures

The old unenclosed woods are the glory of the New Forest. In them can be seen magnificent trees with a beauty of form which, despite their loveliness in summer, can be seen to best advantage in winter when the symmetry of the branches is fully revealed and the pattern of light and shade on the boles is enhanced in wintry sunshine.

These ancient woods are mainly beech. D. W. Young, who

was Deputy-Surveyor for a number of years, stated that the proportion of oaks is often under 15 per cent although sometimes up to 50 per cent. Many of these trees are long past maturity and fallen giants are a common sight. Frustrating as this may be to the forester it is most satisfying to the naturalist. The hollow trunks of erect but ancient trees contain many a nesting hole for the tit and woodpecker families; the fallen logs provide a habitat for many insects. Forester and naturalist, however, can find common ground in deploring the scarcity of regeneration, a tragedy which is now being rectified, none too soon, by the small inclosures constructed for this purpose under the 1949 Act.

Ridley Wood is one such ancient wood. It lies on Barton Sand in a hollow to the east of Picket Post, and being off the beaten track it is largely unfrequented by visitors, not the least of its virtues. A description of its structure can be taken as representative of other woods of this type. It consists of large pollarded beeches with an occasional oak, and has an abundant underwood of shrubby holly. Wide clearings open up the wood but the dense litter of beech leaves prevents the growth of all but the scantiest of field layers. In the wetter parts, societies of water pepper *Polygonum hydropiper* make the lush green patches rising from the leaf mould. Occasional clumps of bramble provide focal points for the woodland butterflies. Other plants include a little ling, bracken and whortleberry near the outskirts and deeper in the wood are scattered plants of foxglove *Digitalis purpurea*, wood sorrel *Oxalis acetosella*, bluebell *Endymion non-scripta*, nettle *Urtica dioica* and celandine *Ranunculus ficaria*.

Holly seedlings are abundant but beech seedlings are rare outside the regeneration inclosure, where they are growing plentifully. Where one is seen elsewhere in the wood others will always be found. No doubt the litter in many places effectually prevents the germination of seed but where the soil is suitable seedlings occur in plenty. Unfortunately many of these are lost due to the grazing of ponies and deer, hence the necessity of the 1949 Act inclosures.

Mosses grow mainly on the banks, round the base of the beeches and on ground devoid of litter. Characteristic species include *Mnium hornum*, *Hypnum cupressiforme*, and the beautiful grey-green cushions of *Leucobryum glaucum*.

In the autumn many species of fungi in a variety of colours decorate the woodland floor and the prostrate trunks of dead beeches. A rare species on beech stumps, *Pluteus chrysophaeus*, has been found in Ridley. The presence of heathland species such as *Lepiota amianthina* and *Paxillus involutus* indicate the acid nature of the soil and these beechwoods clearly correspond to Tansley's vegetational type, *Fagetum ericetosum*.

The prostrate trunks hold a high population of invertebrates. If the bark is lifted the first animal to be exposed is the wood louse *Armadillidium* spp. Next, centipedes, millipedes, earth worms and one at least of the ground beetles are likely to be encountered. Red beetles of the genus *Elater* and, in the Longicorns, *Leptura scutellata* and the wasp beetle *Clytus aristis* frequent decayed stumps. Beetle larvae play an important part in breaking down the wood and returning it to the soil. Such larvae include those of the stag beetle *Lucanus cervus*, the adult of which can sometimes be found crawling in old beech stumps.

Various wasps share the work of decomposition. I have taken the tree wasp *Vespa sylvestris* from a prostrate beech in Ridley Wood and the digger wasp *Coelocrabro leucostomus* from a similar situation in Berry Beeches. The nest of the former is a most conspicuous pear-shaped object. Two species of flies, both Syrphids, haunt decaying beeches. One is *Brachypalpus bimaculatus* and the other is *Calliprobola speciosa*, a distinctive fly of local distribution.

Mature and healthy beeches have their quota of insect life. A Neuropteron common in the area is *Hemorobius micans*, found chiefly on the foliage of beech. Two micromoths which inhabit beech woods are *Ernarmonia aspidiscena* and *Peronea sparsana*. The barred hook tip *Drepana cultraria* and the lobster moth *Stauropus fagi* are characteristic. The brambling, the bird of beech mast, is seldom seen in the New Forest.

Most of the woodlands consist of Forestry Commission inclosures. These contain a considerable variety of tree species although conifers predominate. A New Forest speciality flowering in some of the rides is the beautiful narrow-leaved lungwort *Pulmonaria longifolia.*

The banks of the inclosures are the haunt of the wood cricket *Nemobius sylvestris*; this is a very local species and the forest is one of its strongholds. Various other members of the Orthoptera can be heard if not always seen. In the New Forest as a whole no fewer than 23 out of the 31 species of Orthoptera are to be found.

These woodlands have long been the hunting ground of butterfly collectors but there is a conviction amongst lepidopterists that things are not what they once were. Entomological magazines of the 1890s refer to the immense numbers of butterflies when even the large tortoiseshell *Nymphalis polychloros* and purple emperor *Apatura iris* were not uncommon and a mile length of dried up brook in Roe Wood is described as being crowded with white admiral, ringlets and five species of fritillaries. This must have been the golden age when there were keepers collecting and professional naturalists living in the area. One wonders, indeed, if Beaulieu Road Station, in its stark isolation on the lonely heath, was not built principally for the benefit of lepidopterists!

Which are the butterflies to be seen today in the inclosures? There are, of course, the browns, that essential but somewhat pedestrian component of the woodland scene. These form the workaday background to the more elegant members of the butterfly world. The speckled wood *Pararge aegeria* is perhaps the most attractive member of the family and a pair of them dancing in rapidly gyrating spirals in a woodland clearing is a pleasant sight.

The inclosures hold four species of fritillaries. In early summer there are the pearl-bordered *Argynnis euphrosyne*, and small pearl-bordered *A. selene*, the latter the more local of the two. The high-brown *A. cydippa* is seen in small numbers in the central woodlands but the silver-washed *A. paphia* is generally common. The variety *valezina* is more plentiful here than anywhere else in the country and it has been estimated to be approximately 10 per cent of the female population.

The common Vanessid butterflies are present although the comma *Polygonia c-album* is subject to marked fluctuation in numbers. For most of the last century it was a very rare butterfly in England, but about the year 1921 it staged a come-back and by 1926 was fairly common in the forest. The area is of course a famous locality for the white admiral *Limenitis camilla* though, like the comma, its numbers vary from season to season. Another woodland butterfly is the Duke of Burgundy fritillary *Hamearis lucina*, a local species found in a few southern inclosures in small numbers. The green-veined white *Pieris napi* and the brimstone *Gonepteryx rhamni* are plentiful in all the inclosures. Four species of skippers, dingy *Erynnis tages*, grizzled *Pyrgus malvae*, large *Augiades venata* and small *Thymelicus sylvestris*, fly in the rides. Purple hairstreaks *Thecla quercus* are seen above oaks.

Apart from the Tortrices a number of macromoths are typical of the oakwoods. They include the merveille du jour *Griposia aprilina*, the scarce merveille du jour *Diphthera alpium*, the light crimson underwing *Catocala promissa*, the dark crimson underwing *C. sponsa*, the great oak beauty *Boarmia roboraria*, the pale oak beauty *B. punctinalis*, and many more. Occasionally when walking through the woods one will stumble on the decaying trunk of an oak studded with holes, the work of the caterpillars of the goat moth *Cossus cossus*.

One of the specialities of the area is the New Forest cicada *Cicadetta montana*. This is a bug of the sub-order Homoptera and is a relict species which remained behind when Britain's land link with the continent was finally broken. It is black with red stripes and has a 'song' bearing a slight resemblance to that of a grasshopper but of finer timbre and higher pitched. It is very scarce although easily overlooked. It had not been seen for a number of years and doubts had arisen about its continued existence when in 1962 it was rediscovered. A survey is now being carried out of its habits and ecology.

Beetles find many a congenial habitat in the woods. On the ground there are various *Carabus* and *Geotrupes* spp. The damp grassy rides are good places in which to use the sweep net. The twigs and rotting branches which bestrew the ground under the trees provide food and shelter for many beetles. The rose chafer *Cetonia aurata* is often regarded as an insect which is becoming less common, but in the forest it remains plentiful. In 1940 a weevil new to Britain, *Apion armatum*, was discovered in Wood Fidley on a plant of yellow vetchling.

Some beetles are particularly associated with conifers. An interesting beetle found here is *Rhinomacer attelaboides*. This is a northern species which spread southwards, reaching the New Forest in 1932. An interesting habit of this species is that it is often found after a forest fire, on conifers with scorched needles. Most of the beetles frequenting conifers are weevils, and some do considerable damage to the trees and consequently to the timber crop. Some such as *Otiorrhynchus singularis* feed on pine needles and stems; others like *Hylobius abietus*, *Myelophilus piniperda* and *Hylastes* spp are bark feeders; yet others, for example *Pissodes pini*, bore into the trunk. Two large Longicorns frequenting pines are *Rhagium bifasciatum* and *R. mordax*. The former is the commoner but I have come across both species in the forest.

The wood ant *Formica rufa* is exceedingly abundant in the inclosures. Their immense conical nests are conspicuous on banks and often there are several in close proximity to each other. A large but rather scarce Hymenopteron of coniferous plantations is the brightly coloured greater horntail *Uloceras gigas*. This bores into the trunks of conifers with its long, slender but penetrating ovipositor. The subsequent larvae are the subject of attacks by an Ichneumon *Rhyssa persuasoria* which with uncanny precision and skill locates the horntail larvae and successfully parasitises them.

Wolf spiders *Lycosa* spp abound in the rides. The large *Pisaura mirabilis* is a common and easily recognised spider, the female carrying the egg cocoon in front in contrast to the Lycosids which carry the cocoon attached to the spinnerets. The genus *Theridion* occurs commonly on undergrowth and jumping spiders of the family *Salticidae* in the rides. *Hyptiotes paradoxus* is a rare spider which is sometimes called the triangle spider because of the unusual shape of the web. It is known to occur in only one or two other places outside the forest. Yew seems to be its most favoured tree but it is found on other dark evergreens. It does not seem to be observed very often and there is probably only a small population. In 1954 I discovered an unusual melanic form of this spider on holly in Rushpole Wood.

The great stretches of woodland provide food and cover for many mammals. Mole-hills can be seen in a number of the inclosures. Shrews, short-tailed voles, bank voles, long-tailed field mice and the yellow-necked mice are to be found. A number of bats occur including the rare Bechstein's bat *Myotis bechsteinii* which was first recorded in Britain from the New Forest village of Burley in 1837. The grey squirrel first arrived in the forest about 1940, presumably from the Bournemouth area where introductions were made in the early 1900s. Numbers killed, rising from 14 in 1940–1 to 11,560 in 1953–4, show the climb of the population to superabundance. The red squirrel existed in varying numbers up to the start of World War II when it declined rapidly; none have been seen since the war. Stoats and weasels are not often seen but are no doubt common enough. Foxes and badgers are plentiful.

Missel thrushes are particularly characteristic birds of the area. Singing from the top of an oak or in undulating flight across the heather they match to perfection the wildness of the scenery. Redstarts are thinly but widely distributed chiefly on the outskirts of the woods. Pied flycatchers are seen on migration but had not nested in the area for over fifty years until 1954 when a pair bred. It is almost impossible to walk through an inclosure without hearing at least once the distinctive call-note of the nuthatch and it is difficult to realise that there are parts of England where it is never seen at all. The other trunk-climbing birds are widely distributed, with the lesser spotted woodpecker the least common.

There are relatively small numbers of pheasant in the inclosures. In the southern part there are a few golden pheasants and golden x Lady Amherst hybrids. In early summer woodcock fly over the rides at dusk uttering their roding calls. For a long time it was a debated point whether or not woodcock carry their young, but W. B. Alexander in his 1935 woodcock inquiry assembled considerable evidence testifying that this occasionally happens. One such incident was reported by a forest keeper who in 1931 saw a woodcock in Broomy Inclosure carry a young bird for a number of yards and then return for a second one.

Woodland predators comprise five species but one is extremely rare. The kestrel is probably the commonest but sparrow hawks are not uncommon although not so often seen. A number of pairs of hobbies nest each year. In most of the larger inclosures the penetrating 'mewing' call of the buzzard can be heard. In

Woodcock by C. F. Tunnicliffe. Reproduced by courtesy of the Forestry Commission from their *New Forest Guide*

some years a pair of its rare relations the honey buzzards arrive to nest.

Crossbills are fairly regular breeders in certain areas of mature Scots pine. In irruption years there are often considerable numbers and they can be seen then even in small isolated pines on the heaths. A pair of siskins nested in 1953 and since then siskins appear to have bred regularly in very small numbers. In 1962 a pair of firecrests were known to have bred and it appears that this bird is now following the same pattern as the siskin and nesting regularly.

Heathland

The general plant structure of heathland has been outlined in Chapter Six and will not be repeated here, but the New Forest heaths have also a number of plants of great interest. Perhaps the most beautiful is the wild gladiolus *Gladiolus illyricus* which has a restricted distribution in a few localities. Elsewhere it occurs only in the Isle of Wight and Dorset. The magenta flowers appear at the end of June and are often hidden under bracken fronds.

The whorled knot-grass *Illecebrum verticillatum* arrived in the forest in the 1930s, its first known station being in the vicinity of Hatchet Pond. It has spread rapidly and occurs in the Forestry Commission nurseries from where no doubt it is transported with the tree seedlings when they are planted out in their final quarters. A rare bedstraw, slender marsh bedstraw *Galium debile*, occurs at Hatchet Pond and near Lyndhurst. The autumn lady's tresses *Spiranthes spiralis* is found in grass bordering heathland in parts of the forest.

Of the non-flowering plants, club mosses are distinctly scarce although the fir club moss *Lycopodium selago* can occasionally be found. The pillwort *Pilularia globulifera* grows on wet heaths. A moss of northern mountains *Bryum alpinum* is found on a heath near Lyndhurst. *Splachnum ampullaceum* is an unusual moss in that it grows on dung; it is uncommon in southern England but has been found on pony dung in various parts of the forest. Mosses abundant on wet heathland are *Polytrichum* spp and *Aulacomnium palustre*. In the ferns the moonwort *Botrychium lunaria* and the adder's tongue *Ophioglossum vulgatum* occur in a few localities but careful search for these small ferns would no doubt reveal more stations.

Outstanding among the butterflies is the silver-studded blue *Plebejus argus* which is on the wing in large numbers from early July, particularly in the southern part of the forest in company with the other common heathland species.

The forest once had its own species of burnet moth, *Zygaena meliloti*. It was identified as a separate species in the late nineteenth century when it was discovered in Stubby Copse, an inclosure some three miles from Brockenhurst, but regrettably it is now extinct. The commonest day-flying moth amongst the bracken in early summer is the brown silver lines *Lithina chlorosata* and as dusk falls on June evenings the brown silver lines is replaced by the gold swift *Hepialus hecta*, the larvae of which feed on bracken roots. The angle shades *Phlogophora meticulosa* is a moth which bears a remarkable resemblance to a fragment of bracken frond and the small angle shades *Euplexia lucipara*, another bracken feeder, also occurs in the New Forest.

In some parts, for example, along the banks of the Ober water from Red Rise to Brockenhurst there are many lichen-covered blackthorn bushes and in the spring when the shrubs are in flower the night-flying sloe carpet *Bapta pictaria* appears. The caterpillars of this and of the sharp-angled peacock *Semiothisa alternata* feed on blackthorn leaves in June and July. These are local species and the forest is one of their special localities.

Many of the beetles encountered are of the sub-order Geodephega, the ground beetles. The colourful tiger beetle *Cicindela campestris* may be seen not infrequently in dry sandy places and the more uncommon *C. sylvatica* has been reported from the sandy ridge between Hasley and Sloden Inclosures. The large Carabids are common and the rare *Feronia kugelanni* has been found in sandpits near Longdown.

More than a third of the species of British ants occur, some of them abundantly, on New Forest heathland. One species has only been found in the New Forest in Britain. This is the workerless ant *Anergates atratulus* which lives in utter dependence in the nests of the square-shouldered ant *Tetramorium caespitum*: the worker caste, so characteristic of the ants as a whole, is missing. Another rare species that occurs in the nests of the square-shouldered ant is Diver's ant *Strongylognathus diveri*. It was not discovered in Britain until 1933 when it was found on Studland Heath. This was the only known locality until 27 August 1954 when it was found in a nest of the square-shouldered ant near Matley Passage. This interesting discovery lends support to the view that this is a relict species of the continental fauna.

The square-shouldered ant is abundant and another of the same size is the erratic ant *Tapinoma erraticum* which may be more plentiful here than in many other places in southern England; its long legs and spasmodic movements are characteristic of the species. All three species of red ants, *Myrmica rubra*, *M. sulcinodis* and *M. scabrinodis* can be found in forest heathland. The hillocks of the yellow hill ant *Acanthomyops flavus* exist in colonies and in the wetter parts show a clear contrast in plant cover from the surrounding vegetation. The large black ant *Formica fusca* can be seen along the grass verges and heather tracks. Their nests are pillaged and the workers kidnapped by the workers of an allied species the blood-red slave maker *F. sanguinea*.

There are many species of solitary wasps and bees; they include sand wasps, mason wasps, spider-hunting wasps and burrowing bees and are far too many to enumerate. Suffice it to say that the New Forest is a paradise for the hymenopterist.

The silken tubes of a burrow spider *Agelena labyrinthica* are a familiar sight amongst the heather and wolf spiders abound. The tiny *Micaria pulicaria* is widespread. A number of rare spiders have been recorded from Beaulieu Heath and a gravel pit on Wilverley Plain is the only known locality in England for *Tegenaria agrestis*.

The common lizard is abundant, being known locally as the furze evvet. The sand lizard is found in the drier parts, especially in the western half of the New Forest. Vipers abound and the area is one of the principal haunts in Britain of the rarest of British snakes, the smooth snake. It was in the vicinity of the forest that the first British specimen was captured in 1853.

The rabbit was plentiful in dry sandy parts until myxomatosis decimated their numbers, but it is now recovering. The hare has never been plentiful and it has a very localised distribution for there are large tracts where it is never seen.

On the areas where heather, whether *Calluna* or *Erica*, is dominant the numbers of birds are extremely limited. In 1934 a survey of breeding bird population in an area of 92 acres at Stoneycross revealed 48 adult birds of which 24 were meadow pipits and 15 were skylarks. The meadow pipit is resident but some flocking takes place in the autumn. Where scattered pines occur which can be used as song-posts, tree pipits and woodlarks breed. The former is well distributed but in line with the national trend the latter has become extremely scarce.

Where the heather has been well burnt the occasional pair of wheatears can be seen. Its requirement of rabbit burrows for nesting purposes and its preference for soil largely denuded of vegetation considerably restricts its range. Garrow's *History of Lymington* published in 1825 imparts the information that the forest wheatears were inferior in flavour to Sussex birds! Such was ornithology 150 years ago.

The mention of gorse to an ornithologist conjures up a picture of a jaunty tail cocked skywards: the dartford warbler. It was widely distributed in scattered localities until almost exterminated by the hard winter of 1963; its recovery since then has been very slow indeed. Whitethroats and stonechats are plentiful in the gorse areas. A small number of whinchats nest. Linnets and yellowhammers are widespread.

Small numbers of common partridge occur and a few red-legged partridges are found in the southern part.

Conservation

Controversy and bitter dispute over various matters have beclouded forest history for at least 150 years. This is not the place to enlarge on that except to say that nature conservation is a new contestant in the debate. It is not yet the victor and things have happened recently which are enough to cause dismay to any nature-lover, but increasingly its voice is heard.

A committee consisting of representatives of the Forestry Commission, the Verderers and the local authorities of the area produced in 1970 an important report *Conservation of the New Forest* which includes recommendations for greater control of the public use of the forest. In October 1970 a Consultative Panel was formed to provide an advisory service to the Forestry Commission, and on this panel nature conservation interests are represented.

There has been considerable concern at some of the recent tree felling and planting and the government minister responsible imposed a temporary ban on hardwood felling. Then on 3 May 1971 he took a momentous step with the announcement that the New Forest must be treated as a national heritage and issued fresh instructions to the Commission not only for the conservation of the ornamental woods but also for the inclosures where hardwood felling and softwood planting are to be greatly restricted.

The basic problem has always been the conflict of irreconcilable interests, but one fact is certain: the New Forest will of necessity always be a multi-use area and any solution must take account of this fact.

CHAPTER NINE

The Isle of Wight

Geological structure–Plants–Invertebrates–Mammals –Birds

THE RELATIVELY LARGE size of the Isle of Wight, coupled with its isolation from the remainder of the region, justifies its having a chapter on its own even though no more than a superficial survey can be undertaken in this space.

A lozenge-shaped island, it stands athwart the entrance of Southampton Water and is separated from the mainland by two arms of the sea, the Solent in the west and Spithead in the east. It has an area of 147 square miles and has 60 miles of coastline. The scenery, both coastal and inland, is exceptionally varied and beautiful, due largely to the underlying geological strata. Not for nothing is it known as the Garden Isle, with its mild climate, high sunshine record and profusion of flowers. The meteorological records show that for the 30 years up to 1960 Sandown has had an average of 1,858 hours of sunshine per year and several other coastal resorts on the island come very close to this record.

Rivers are not numerous and apart from the estuarial sections, are small in size. The north shore has a few drowned river valleys, notably the river Yar, Newtown Creek, the river Medina at Cowes, Wootton Creek and Bembridge Harbour.

The south coast consists of Cretaceous cliffs passing through Gault, Greensand and Wealden but beginning in the west with the superb chalk cliffs of Scratchell's Bay and ending with the chalk of Culver Cliff. These cliffs are broken by a number of chines and the south-east section has an under-cliff of broken rock where the upper strata have slipped on the impervious Gault Clay.

A spectacular cliff fall, a photograph of which appears on page 143, took place at Gore Cliff near Niton on 26 July 1928 when an estimated 150,000–200,000 tons tumbled from the vertical cliff face, followed by a further collapse in September of that year. The July fall buried the road and in the second incident the earth pressure was so great that the promontory of Rocken End was forced into the sea. A much more recent slip, though of smaller dimensions, occurred in March 1957 at Scratchell's Bay when 20,000 tons of chalk crashed into the sea, crushing numbers of seabirds in the process.

On the west coast at Alum Bay is a remarkable cliff face consisting of coloured sands of vertical Eocene strata which run through the whole gamut from the Barton to the Reading beds and are used commercially in souvenirs.

There is a considerable extent of downland in the central part, at Freshwater in the south-west and between Chale and Ventnor in the south-east where a large outlier of chalk reaches 787ft at St Boniface Down. The island is liberally besprinkled with small woods and there are two larger woodland tracts, Parkhurst Forest in the north and Brighstone Forest on the central downland ridge.

Geology

Geologically the Isle of Wight is essentially the southern part of the Hampshire synclinal basin. The northern half consists of soft Tertiary rocks equating those on the adjacent part of the mainland, with the addition of a number of beds of the Oligocene period, the Headon, Osborne, Bembridge and Hamstead beds. The Headon beds occur over a considerable area of the New Forest and the adjacent coastal strip but the remaining beds of the Upper Oligocene are, in the British Isles, virtually confined to the Isle of Wight. The southern half comprises Cretaceous rocks of Chalk, Gault and Greensand with smaller areas of Wealden shales and marls, as on the Dorset coast.

Even a casual glance at a geological map will at once prompt the thought that these two formations of chalk must once have been joined. The same conclusion is reached if one looks from the top of Hengistbury Head, first south-eastwards to the chalk pinnacles of the Needles and then south-westwards to where the chalk pinnacles are duplicated in the Old Harry rocks at Studland as Ballard Down steps into the sea. In comparatively recent times, geologically speaking, this continuous line of chalk ramparts guarded the ancient Solent river from the sea. Then, several thousand years BC, the hungry sea succeeded in breaching the chalk and soon cliff and river had been engulfed by the waves and the Isle of Wight was born.

Many of the beds are rich in fossils. Ammonites, corals, crustaceans, sea urchins, fish, reptilian remains, insects, lamellibranchs, gastropods and brachiopods occur in profusion, many of them rare elsewhere. Fossils are found in most strata from the estuarine molluscs in the Upper Hamstead beds at Bouldnor Cliff to the fish and reptilian remains in the Wealden marls at Sandown and Brighstone Bay. Remains of a submerged forest can be seen at low water at Hanover Point, near Brook. Interesting discoveries continue to be made as, for instance, that of a rare fossil fish *Belonostomos hooleyi* unearthed at Atherfield Point in 1964.

Drilling for oil took place at Arreton Down on the Sandown anticline in 1952 but this proved abortive as very little oil was located.

Plants

As the scenery is varied so is the vegetation. Well over a thousand species of flowering plants and ferns have been recorded and the total is little less than that of the adjacent county of Hampshire. The island is particularly rich in flowers of the coast.

Newtown Marsh on the north-west shore is a local nature reserve of the Isle of Wight County Council. Within its boundaries 216 species of plants have been recorded. There are several habitats within the reserve but the principal one is salt marsh. Here grow the typical salt marsh species including cord grass *Spartina townsendii*, English scurvy grass *Cochlearia anglica*, golden samphire *Inula crithmoides*, sea aster *Aster tripolium*, glass-wort *Salicornia* spp, and the beautiful marsh mallow *Althaea officinalis*.

On the north-east shore at St Helens there are dunes backed by short turf where the little autumn squill *Scilla autumnalis* flowers in August and September in its only locality on the island or for that matter, on the adjacent mainland either. Other plants growing here are the tree lupin *Lupinus arboreus*, sea buckthorn *Hippophae rhamnoides*, sea holly *Eryngium maritimum*, sea bindweed *Calystegia soldanella* and evening primrose *Oenothera stricta*. The sea heath *Frankenia laevis* has been recorded from St Helens Spit; this prostrate plant is not common on the south coast but grows more plentifully on the shores of East Anglia.

Just south of St Helens lies Bembridge with a rocky shore rich in seaweeds and marine life. The common brown seaweeds have a definite lineal zonation on beaches and in descending order are: flat wrack *Fucus spiralis*, knotted wrack *Ascophyllum nodosum*, bladder wrack *Fucus vesiculosus*, serrated wrack *Fucus serratus* and tangle weed *Laminaria digitata*. These are widely distributed, but Bembridge also has some rather less common brown sea-weeds such as the heather-fronded *Cystoseira tamariscifolia*, *Halidrys siliquosa* and the fan-shaped *Padina pavonia*. Various species of green and red seaweed grow on the lower levels of the shore.

Seaweed en masse can be a problem to a tourist-orientated seaside resort and there has been such a problem at East Cowes. A survey was authorised and carried out in the summer of 1969. It was found that as well as the weed growing locally, there were species which had been washed up from other places, some from inter-tidal beds elsewhere in the Solent and some possibly from as far afield as the French coast. Various recommendations were made to deal with the problem.

There are fine cliffs at Freshwater in the west and Culver Cliff in the east where the chalk ridge reaches the coast. Here grow a number of interesting flowers of which the most notable is the hoary stock *Matthiola incana*, growing high on the cliffs between Compton and Freshwater in places difficult of access. This was formerly considered to be the only station in the British Isles but while it still remains the principal locality the plant is now known to exist in a few other places in southern England and at one spot in the North East. Opinions vary on whether it is truly native. There is no doubt about the naturalised status of the sweet alison *Lobularia maritima* which grows in the vicinity. The sea carrot *Daucus carota gummifer* and the white horehound *Marrubium vulgare* grow here and elsewhere on the island.

The cliff top at Freshwater has the rare tufted centaury *Centaurium capitatum*. The combination of shallow soil and proximity to the sea has here produced exceptionally stunted plants of a number of species including hairy rock cress *Arabis hirsuta*, yellow-wort *Blackstonia perfoliata* and betony *Betonica officinalis*. At Culver the Portland spurge *Euphorbia portlandica* grows not only at the base of the cliff but ascends high up. A variety of calcareous plants provide a colourful display in summer, the bright yellow of horseshoe vetch *Hippocrepis comosa*, the butter yellow of rock rose *Helianthemum chamaecistus*, the pale pink of the tiny squinancywort *Asperula cynanchica* and the lilac blue of small scabious *Scabiosa columbaria*.

The undercliff from Chale to Ventnor with its tumbled masses of rocks has a fine variety of shrubs and flowers. The presence of the Gault has caused wet ill-drained areas where after a cliff fall bare ground is often colonised by great horsetail *Equisetum telmateia* and coltsfoot *Tussilago farfara*. Distinctive flowers include: tall melilot *Melilotus altissima*, kidney vetch *Anthyllis vulneraria*, ivy broomrape *Orobanche hederae*, slender birdsfoot trefoil *Lotus tenuis* and madder *Rubia peregrina*.

In addition to the typical plants of chalk downs already listed in a previous chapter the central chalk ridge in the Isle of Wight has two rare plants. One is the wood calamint *Calamintha sylvatica*, which in the British Isles is found only in the Isle of Wight. It was first discovered by the botanist Dr Bromfield in August 1843. The flowers and leaves are relatively large, and the deep colouring of the former with the lilac overlaid with deep purple on the lip, make the common calamint flowers look pale and washed-out by comparison. The other is field fleawort *Senecio integrifolius*, a very local species which grows at Brighstone. This is a plant of cultivation and it has been suggested that it may have been brought in by Iron Age settlers. It is seldom more than 6in high, possessing the yellow flowers of the wild and cultivated *Senecios* but, unlike many of the native species, having lanceolate leaves.

Woods in the northern part of the island have lungwort *Pulmonaria longifolia* which grows also in the clayey rides of the New Forest. The stinking iris *Iris foetidissima* is common in many of the woods and occurs plentifully along the undercliff also. In light shade in small woods and roadsides near Ventnor grows the Italian cuckoo-pint *Arum neglectum*. It was first discovered in this locality which for a long time was believed to be its only station in the British Isles. It is now known, however, to exist in a number of other places in southern England.

The Isle of Wight helleborine *Epipactis phyllanthes* var. *vectensis* was also found in a wood near Ventnor in 1917 and that too was at first thought to be restricted to the island. In recent years it has been discovered within the central southern region on the Hampshire mainland and in Berkshire and outside the region in several other counties. It is not known, however, outside the British Isles. It is self-pollinated without the flowers opening.

Ventnor is well favoured where uncommon plants are concerned. Not far from there the field cow-wheat *Melampyrum arvense* was common in cornfields in the middle of the last century but now it is known only from one grass bank where in 1964 it was necessary to erect a fence to protect it against cows. Townsend records that it was once so abundant that bread was sometimes discoloured by its presence with the grains of wheat. So the pest of one century has become the rarity of the next.

Invertebrates

The dry mild climate is ideal for crickets and grasshoppers. The green grasshopper *Omocestus viridulus*, the wood cricket *Nemobius sylvestris* and native cockroaches *Ectobius* spp are found in woods; the south-facing slopes of the downs have the field cricket *Gryllus campestris*, the stripe-winged grasshopper *Stenobothrus lineatus* and *Chorthippus* spp; the grey bush cricket *Platycleis denticulata* and the great green grasshopper *Tettigonia viridissima* are frequent in thickets and in rough vegetation on the southern cliffs where also can be found the rare long-winged cone-head *Conocephalus discolor*. Its relative, *C. dorsalis* is frequent in its salt-marsh habitat.

The island has a good variety of butterflies. Parkhurst Forest not only has the four fritillaries of woodland, white admirals, skippers and other common species but also the large tortoiseshell *Vanessa polychloros* now seldom seen on the Hampshire mainland and scarce in the remainder of the region. Marbled whites *Melanargia galatea*, dark green fritillaries *Argynnis aglaia*, grayling *Eumenis semele*, chalkhill blue *Lysandra coridon* and adonis blue *L. bellargus* frequent the downs.

The undercliff with its tangle of vegetation and its slope towards the sun is clearly a paradise for butterflies. Here one may expect to find the immigrant Vanessids making landfall, the painted lady *Vanessa cardui*, the peacock *V. io* and the red admiral *V. atalanta*. I have seen near Blackgang numbers of that more irregular immigrant the clouded yellow *Colias croceus* and with them one of the pale coloured variety *helice*. Resident butterflies plentiful here include the wall *Pararge megera*, common blue *Polyommatus icarus*, holly blue *Celastrina argiolus*, small blue *Cupido minimus* and small copper *Lycaena phlaeas*.

There remains the famous speciality of the undercliff, the glanville fritillary *Melitaea cinxia*. This beautiful insect, which somewhat resembles the small pearl-bordered fritillary, was first discovered on the Isle of Wight coast in 1824. It has occurred in a few places in south-east England but the principal and now the only locality in Britain is the south coast of the Isle of Wight. Here on the undercliff the larvae feed on plantains and the butterflies frequent the flowers of kidney vetch. It has disappeared from some of its former haunts but is still locally common. A striking example of butterfly vagrants was the American painted lady *Vanessa virginiensis* which turned up on the island in August 1956, only the thirteenth of this species recorded in Britain.

It is not proposed to list moths which have already been mentioned in connection with various mainland habitats but to refer briefly to a few especially associated with the Isle of Wight. A number of coastal species are found on the cliffs particularly at Freshwater. Here in abundance and at Ventnor is the little dew moth *Setina irrorella*, its buff forewings delicately dotted with black spots. The caterpillars feed on the lichens which clothe the rocks. The square-spot dart *Euxoa obelisca* has one of its principal localities on the Freshwater cliffs where it flies in late summer. To the non-entomologist the Isle of Wight wave *Sterrha humiliata* is a small and insignificant moth, but the lepidopterist finds it exciting enough for it is a southern European species whose one slender foothold in the British Isles is on the island cliffs, another indication of the mildness of the climate. It was first discovered in 1891 and is closely related to that other very localised moth of Dorset, the Portland ribbon wave *S. degeneraria*. The annulet *Gnophos obscurata* is a moth of wide distribution both inland and coastal but with a definite preference for habitats near the sea. This species provides an interesting example of cryptic coloration, existing on southern heaths and Scottish mountains in a dark form but on the chalk cliffs near the Needles as a white form.

Below the high chalk cliffs in Freshwater Bay there is a small area of salt-marsh. Here since World War II some remarkable discoveries have been made by Dr K. G. Blair, the retired Deputy Keeper of Entomology at the British Museum of Natural History. In 1945 he found a wainscot new to Britain, *Sedina buettneri*, whose larvae live in the stems of the lesser pond sedge *Carex acutiformis*. Subsequently he made more discoveries adding Blair's mocha *Cosymbia pupillaris* and Blair's shoulder knot *Lithophane leautieri* to the British list. The last named which was found on 26 October 1951, was subsequently found on the Hampshire mainland from 1960 onwards and for some years now has appeared in numbers in the New Forest and the Itchen valley. The larvae feed on *Cupressus macrocarpa*.

The moths of the downs include the feathered brindle *Aporophyla australis*, the light feathered rustic *Agrotis cinerea* and two very local plume moths *Alucita spilodactyla* and *Leioptilus carphodactylus*, the larvae of the former feeding on white horehound and of the latter on the carline thistle. The caterpillars of the reddish buff *Acosmetia caliginosa* feed on the leaves of saw-wort in damp meadows and the moth which is now rare still occurs in the western part of the island. On the Hampshire mainland it has not been recorded since 1961. The vestal *Rhodometra sacraria* is a small distinctively-coloured moth with yellow forewings each carrying an oblique crimson stripe. A native of Mediterranean countries, in some years it migrates northwards; in Britain it is a rare immigrant but can be seen most years in some of the island stubble fields in late summer.

About half of the total number of species of British beetles occur in the Isle of Wight. The undercliff is a very good locality for beetles both common and rare. There are many common Carabids but there is also a tiger beetle *Cicindela germanica* found at the foot of the cliffs at Blackgang Chine but not in many other places in Britain. An even rarer ground beetle is *Chlaenius nitidulus*, a beautiful insect which has been recorded from Luccombe Chine. The unstable nature of the undercliff, however, and the resulting effect on even small creatures, is illustrated by the destruction of this beetle's habitat when one of the falls took place. Of better known beetles the two bloody-nosed beetles *Timarcha tenebricosa* and *T. goettingensis* and the glow-worm *Lampyris noctiluca* may be mentioned.

In certain places along the southern coast of the island are small waterfalls and here live certain beetles particularly associated with this habitat, for example *Dianous coerulescens* and *Lesteva* spp in moss, and *Elmis maugei* under stones. Another Isle of Wight speciality is a tiny weevil *Baris analis* which feeds on fleabane and has been recorded from the base of the Sandown cliffs.

If looked for, numbers of beetles can be discovered on the seashore. The island has its own variety of a small beetle *Bembidion saxatile*; this is *vectensis* and is found on the shingle shores of the southern coast. Of freshwater habitat, the great silver water beetle *Hydrous piceus*, the largest of the water beetles and a scarce insect, has been recorded from the island in recent years. The importation of timber has brought in alien species and in 1946 three longhorn beetles of a species new to Britain, *Trinophyllum cribatum*, were discovered at East Cowes. Since then the beetle has spread and now occurs in other parts of Britain.

Parkhurst Forest is not perhaps outstanding for insects but it has a number of interesting spiders. *Myrmarachne formicaria*, as its name implies, bears a resemblance to an ant and sometimes associates with them. *Phrarolithus minimus* is a small sun-loving spider only 2·5mm in size, and is recorded from only a few places in Britain, two of which are on the island—at Parkhurst and a wood near Wootton. *Lycosa paludicola* is a wolf spider within the region, known only from Parkhurst.

Mammals and reptiles

The common British mammals occur, with the exception of grey squirrels and deer. There have, however, been rumours in recent months of a deer in the Newtown area, and if these are correct it is likely to be a roe which has swum the Solent. Otters still survive, and although it is often stated that the Isle of Wight has no badgers I am informed that there is, in fact, a substantial badger population. In the world of mammals, however, the chief interest of the island to the naturalist lies with the red squirrels, which are fairly common and well distributed, particularly in the northern woods. The island of Brownsea is now the only other place within the region where red squirrels still exist.

Frogs and toads have been the subjects of a series of methodical and meticulous surveys carried out by local naturalists between 1964 and 1970. The results have shown that frog numbers have declined greatly in the west and south-west of the island but that the decline has not been so pronounced in the north and east. Toads appear to be holding their own.

Of the lizards the slow-worm and the common lizard are fairly plentiful but the sand-lizard is not known. A strong colony of wall-lizards was discovered soon after 1960 in one part of the island, and it is probable that these have originated from introductions made by Lord Walsingham in 1899.

Birds

For the bird-watcher the coastline holds the greatest interest. The estuaries of Yarmouth, Newtown and Bembridge have their complement of ducks and waders. Of these, Newtown, a local nature reserve with a nature trail, is the showpiece. Its ornithological interest has increased in recent years; until 27 November 1954 the marsh had been for centuries grazing land for cattle, but on that night of violent storm the sea broke through the defences and has taken possession of the former pasture. Nesting birds include shelduck, black-headed gull and oyster-catcher, but of course it is in the autumn and winter that the largest numbers and greatest variety of species are seen. There is here the largest gathering of wigeon on the Isle of Wight, with numbers up to 500. Birds regularly seen at that time include mallard, teal, wigeon, red-breasted merganser, shelduck, oyster-catcher, redshank, curlew, black-tailed godwit and dunlin.

An impressive list of irregular visitors has been recorded including garganey, pintail, golden-eye, brent goose, marsh harrier, hen harrier, osprey, little stint, curlew-sandpiper, avocet, grey phalarope, little gull, short-eared owl and snow bunting.

At Main Bench near the Needles are nesting colonies of sea birds. The auks have greatly declined since the beginning of World War II; guillemots are down to less than one-tenth of their population twenty-five years ago; a similar state of affairs exists with the razorbills, and puffins are reduced to a mere handful. On the credit side, fulmars began prospecting as long ago as 1953, but although they have been regular in summer ever since, breeding still remains to be proved. More speedy success has been achieved by the kittiwakes. One bird was seen in the summer of 1966 on the Freshwater cliffs. In 1969 eight pairs were known to have nested and a year later this total had expanded to twenty-five pairs. One or two pairs of great black backed gulls usually nest, and there is a strong colony of herring gulls both here and at Culver Cliff. Cormorants and, in very much smaller numbers, shags nest at Freshwater. There are still two pairs of ravens left on the island. Peregrines bred regularly on these cliffs until about the mid 1950s; in 1955 nesting took place both at Culver and Freshwater, but breeding has not been known since.

Near Cowes the grounds of Osborne House slope to the sea and this parkland where once Queen Victoria delighted to stroll provides a suitable habitat for many species. There are jays, marsh tits and tree creepers, augmented in summer by leaf warblers, blackcaps and to a lesser extent garden warblers. Jackdaws are plentiful and collared doves took up residence in 1966. More unexpected birds seen in this royal park have been ring-ouzels and crossbills.

The green woodpecker was surprisingly late in arriving. At the beginning of the century the bird was virtually unknown on the island. It first bred in 1910, and by 1920 had become a common breeding bird. It was reduced in numbers by the 1963 hard winter but is now making a come-back. The wren was another hard-hit species, and an account exists of fifty-one wrens roosting in one nest box near Newport in January 1963. Two woodland birds which are unaccountably scarce on the Isle of Wight are the tawny owl and the nuthatch. On inland waters moorhens are plentiful but coot and little grebe are scarce as breeders. Kingfishers frequent the rivers and in 1970 a mandarin duck nested successfully at Alverstone, near Sandown.

The Isle of Wight has been one of the few localities of the dartford warbler, and despite its great decline one or two birds are still being observed. The continued survival of this bird, symbol of the Hampshire and Isle of Wight Naturalists' Trust, may perhaps be hopefully taken as a sign that despite the inordinate pressures of civilisation in a densely populated region, the wild life of southern England continues resurgent.

Dartford warbler by C. F. Tunnicliffe. Reproduced by courtesy of the Forestry Commission from their *New Forest Guide*

Appendix

Areas of natural history interest

A FEW LOCAL NATURE reserves have been omitted for the sake of the rarities they contain. Note that for a few reserves listed here access is not permitted or is restricted, and that a permit is required in many other cases. The listing of a locality does not necessarily indicate a right of access, and responsibility rests with the intending visitor to observe the necessary courtesies and obtain permission where such is required.

List of abbreviations

BBONT	Berkshire, Buckinghamshire and Oxfordshire Naturalists' Trust
CBC	Christchurch Borough Council
DNT	Dorset Naturalists' Trust
FC	Forestry Commission
FNR	Forest Nature Reserve
HNT	Hampshire and Isle of Wight Naturalists' Trust
HCC	Hampshire County Council
IOWCC	Isle of Wight County Council
LNR	Local Nature Reserve
NNR	National Nature Reserve
NT	National Trust
PBC	Portsmouth Borough Council
RSPB	Royal Society for the Protection of Birds
SPNR	Society for the Promotion of Nature Reserves
SSSI	Site of Special Scientific Interest
STNC	Somerset Trust for Nature Conservation
WBC	Weymouth Borough Council
WTNC	Wiltshire Trust for Nature Conservation

Berkshire

Ashley Hill, north-east of Reading. FC woodland. Fallow and muntjac.
Bagley Wood, south-west of Oxford. Grid SI 5103. Good entomological locality.

Bearwood Lake, south-east of Reading. SU 7768. Ornithological interest.
Cothill Fen, south-west of Oxford. SU 4699. Part LNR, BBONT; part NNR. Rich fen flora and insect life.
Dry Sandford Quarry, south-west of Oxford. SU 4699. LNR, BBONT, SSSI. Good geological section of the Corallian Limestone and varied flora.
Englefield Lake, west of Reading. SU 6372. Ornithological interest.
Ham Island Bird Sanctuary, south-east of Windsor. SU 9973. 100 acres. Managed by Middle Thames Natural History Society.
Hurley Chalk Pit, east of Henley-on-Thames. SU 8182. LNR, ½ acre. Chalk flowers and fossils.
Inkpen Beacon, Hampshire–Berkshire border. SU 3763. Downland birds and butterflies.
Inkpen Common, north-west of Newbury. SU 3864. LNR, BBONT, 26 acres. Heathland flowers and birds.
Moor Copse, Tidmersh. SU 6374. LNR, BBONT, 56 acres. Damp woodland. Permit required.
Newbury, commons around the town. Heathland insects.
Shellingford Pond, south-east of Farringdon. SU 3293. LNR, BBONT, 5 acres. Damp woodland with rich cryptogrammic plant life.
Silchester Common, south-west of Reading. Good entomological locality.
Thatcham Moor, east of Newbury. SU 5367. SSSI. Extensive reed-beds of ornithological interest.
Theale Gravel Pit, west of Reading. SU 6471. Ornithological interest.
Virginia Water. SU 9769. Ornithological interest.
Watchfield Common Wood, Vale of White Horse. SU 2291. LNR, BBONT, 22 acres. Elm-dominated nutrient-rich woodland bordering the river Cole. Variety of woodland plants and kingfishers.
White Horse Vale Downs. SU 3187. Downland butterflies. Bird migration route.
Windsor Forest, High Standing Hill. SU 9374. FNR, 45 acres. Old deciduous woodland rich in rare invertebrate life.
Wytham Wood, near Oxford. SP 4608. Mixed deciduous woodland. Used by Oxford University for field studies.

Dorset

Abbotsbury, north-west of Weymouth. Famous swannery open in summer· Admission charge.
Arne, southern shore of Poole Harbour, SY 9788. RSPB reserve, 700 acres. Dartford warblers. Permit required.
Arne, SY 9788. NNR, 9 acres. Woodland abutting on salt marsh. Permit required.
Blackdown, south-west of Dorchester. Heathland plant and animal life.

Black Ven, east of Lyme Regis, SY 3593. LNR, DNT, 27 acres. Land-slips, plant-recolonisation.
Blashenwell, near Corfe, SY 9781. Geological interest; calcareous tufa containing Mesolithic flints.
Bradford Peverell Down, north-west of Dorchester, SY 6493. LNR, DNT. Chalk-pit and grassland. Permit required.
Brownsea Island (part of), in Poole Harbour, SZ 0288. LNR, DNT, 250 acres. Heronry, ternery, red squirrels. Guided tours for public during summer.
Chesil Beach and the Fleet, west of Weymouth. SSSI. Geological interest. Shingle-beach flora, ternery, winter wildfowl. No access in summer to ternery.
Chickerell, Crook Hill Brick Pit, SY 6581. SSSI. Fossil locality.
Chickerell, Putton Lane Brick Pit, SY 6581. SSSI. Fine exposure of Kellaways beds, fossil reptilian remains.
Cranbourne Chase, north-east of the county. Large blocks of woodland. Fallow, sika, roe.
Durlston Bay, Swanage, SZ 0477. Geological interest. Sea-bird colonies, grass-hoppers, early spider orchid.
East Stoke Fen, west of Wareham, SY 8686. LNR, DNT, 11 acres. Reed bed and marsh carr. Permit required.
Ferrybridge, Portland, SY 6778. Ornithological interest at migration times.
Gillingham Brick Pit, ST 8125. Selenite crystals, reptilian remains, ammonites etc in Kimmeridge Clay.
Green Hill Down, south-west of Blandford, ST 7903. LNR, DNT. Down and woodland. Chalk butterflies, roe deer. Access restricted.
Hartland Moor, south-east of Wareham, SY 9585. NNR, 640 acres. Heathland flora including Dorset heath. Permit required.
Hod Hill, ST 8511. LNR, DNT, 6½ acres. Downland butterflies.
Holway Coppices, ST 6319. LNR, DNT, 15 acres. Deciduous woodland. Restricted access.
Isle of Purbeck, whole peninsula of great interest for its insects, mammals and fossils.
Jerry's Hole, ST 8716. LNR, DNT, 7 acres. Downland flora and fauna. Permit required.
Kilwood, SY 9382. LNR, DNT, ½ acre. Orchid locality. Permit required.
Little Bredy, west of Dorchester. Field of conglomerate boulders.
Littledown, ST 9910. LNR, DNT, 4 acres. Downland flora and fauna.
Lulworth, SY 8380. Cliff-formations, fossil forest, Lulworth skipper.
Lodmoor, Weymouth, SY 6882. Entomological and ornithological interest.
Lyme-Regis–Charmouth. SSSI. Classic cliff-section of Lower Lias rich in many types of fossils.
Morden Bog, north of Wareham, SY 9193. NNR, 367 acres. Woodland, heath

and bog. Rich bog flora and fauna, smooth snake and sand lizard. Permit required.
Newlands Batch, SY 3993. LNR, DNT, 100 acres. Coastal reserve. Restricted access.
Poole Harbour. Waders and winter wildfowl including golden-eye, mergansers and grebes.
Portland Bill, SY 6868. Great geological interest, fossils. Sea-bird colonies, rare migrants, sea-watch point.
Radipole Lake, Weymouth, SY 6781. LNR, WBC, 70 acres. Outstanding ornithological interest.
Ringstead, SY 7682. SSSI. Geological interest. Cretaceous overstep on upturned Jurassic strata.
St Gabriel's Bank, SY 4093. LNR, DNT, 1 acre. Coastal reserve, orchids.
Studland, south of Poole, SZ 0485. NNR, 429 acres. Mainly heath and sand dunes with the large freshwater lagoon of Littlesea. Singing sands. Great variety of plant and animal life.
West Bexington, SY 5287. LNR, DNT, 40 acres. Coastal marsh of ornithological interest, particularly migration.
Whitenothe, SY 7681. LNR, DNT, 115 acres. Undercliff, plant-colonisation. Dangerous to leave path. Good locality for ammonites etc.
Wool Marsh, SY 8487. LNR, DNT, 2 acres. Freshwater marsh. Permit required.
Woolsbarrow, SY 8992. LNR, DNT, 11 acres. Heathland fauna. Restricted access.

Hampshire and Isle of Wight

Alresford Pond, SU 5933. LNR of HNT. Winter wildfowl, entomological interest. Permit required.
Alum Bay, Isle of Wight. Coloured sands, fine vertical Tertiary section.
Atherfield Point, Isle of Wight, SZ 4579. Good fossil locality.
Avington Lake, SU 5333. Surface-feeding ducks.
Avon Valley, Ringwood–Fordingbridge. Flock of white-fronted geese, pintail.
Barton Cliffs. Five miles of highly fossiliferous Tertiary strata with crocodile, fish and mammalian remains.
Black Point, Hayling Island, SZ 7598. Sanderling. Chichester Harbour Brent flock.
Bouldnor Cliff, Isle of Wight, SZ 3891. Highly fossiliferous Oligocene strata.
Bournemouth Bay. Large flocks of common scoter in winter.
Brading Marsh, Isle of Wight, SZ 6388. Wildfowl.
Bramshaw, New Forest, SU 2516. FNR, 525 acres. Old deciduous woodland.
Brook Bay, Isle of Wight, SZ 3783. Submerged fossil forest.
Burghclere Old Lime Works, SU 4757. LNR, HNT. Plant-colonisation in quarry. Permit required.

Catherington Down, SU 6914. LNR, HNT and HCC. Public open space. Downland flora.
Cherque, Lee-on-Solent, SU 5701. LNR, HNT. Varied habitats abutting on the river Alver.
Crabwood (part of), Sparsholt, SU 4330. LNR, HNT. Hazel coppice for use as educational reserve.
Culver Cliff, Isle of Wight, SZ 6385. Cretaceous fossils. Herring-gull colonies, cliff flora.
Curbridge, SU 5211. LNR, HNT, NT. Wood and salt marsh bordering the river Hamble.
Danebury Hill, SU 3337. HCC. Public open space. Good chalk flora.
Farlington Marshes, SU 6804. LNR, PBC managed by HNT. Rare salt-marsh plants. Outstanding ornithological interest.
Freshwater Down, Isle of Wight, SZ 3285 and 3385. Chalk flora.
Gilkicker Point, SZ 6097. Migration watch-point.
Hawkley Warren, SU 7328. LNR, HNT. Mixed woodland.
Hengistbury Head, SZ 1790. Bird-ringing station.
Hythe Spartina beds, SU 4307. LNR, HNT. Reserve for spartina study. No access.
Keyhaven, SZ 3190. LNR, HNT. Ornithological interest. No access during nesting season.
Kingfisher Lake, Blashford, SU 1607. Good wildfowl locality.
Leckford, on river Test, SU 3737. Wintering wildfowl.
Long Aldermoor, New Forest, SU 2709. LNR, HNT. Mixed 'wet' habitats. Permit required.
Mark Ash, New Forest, SU 2407. FNR, 226 acres. Beechwood.
Matley and Denny. FNR, 257 acres. New Forest.
Needs Oar, SZ 4297. Private reserve. Sea-bird colonies. Permit required.
New Forest. 105 square miles of Crown Land in south-west corner of the county, outstanding for its wealth of plant and animal life.
Newtown Marsh, Isle of Wight, SZ 4291. LNR, IOWCC. Good salt-marsh flora and ornithological interest. Permit required.
Old Winchester Hill, SU 6421. NNR, 140 acres. Chalk down and woodland, primarily of botanical interest.
Oxenbourne Down, SU 7118. LNR, HNT. Chalk down and woodland. Permit required.
Pennington Marshes, SZ 3394. Ornithological interest.
Portsdown Hill, SU 6406 and 6506. Geological feature. Downland flowers and insects.
Quarley Hill, SU 2642. Stone curlew migration.
St Catherine's Point, Isle of Wight, SZ 4975. Migration watch-point. Fossil locality.
Scratchell's Bay, Isle of Wight, SZ 2984 and 3084. Sea-bird colonies. Cliff flora.

Selborne Hanger, SU 7433. Beech hanger with Gilbert White associations. Whole village of interest and well worth a pilgrimage.
Sowley Pond, SZ 3897. Good wildfowl locality. Heronry.
Stanpit Marsh, Christchurch, SZ 1792. LNR, CBC, 145 acres. Good ornithological locality.
The Chase, Woolton Hill, SU 4462. LNR, HNT. Mixed woodland. Permit required.
Titchfield Haven, SU 5403. Private reserve. Ornithological interest. No access.
Undercliff, Isle of Wight. Rich botanical and entomological locality along the southern coast.
Upper Titchfield Haven, SU 5403. LNR, HNT. Marshland. Permit required.
Whitecliff Bay, Isle of Wight, SZ 6486. Fine Tertiary section and good fossil locality.

Somerset

Asham Wood, ST 7045. LNR, STNC, 38 acres. Hazel coppice with oak standards. Rich flora, nightingales, wood white butterflies and mountain bulin snail. Permit required.
Avon Gorge, ST 5673. Great botanical and geological interest.
Bath. Spiked star of Bethlehem in woods around city.
Berrow Sand Dunes. Good sand dune flora and fauna.
Black Rock, ST 4854. LNR, STNC, 121 acres. Woodland and pasture. Permit required.
Blagdon Reservoir, ST 5260. 430 acres. Great ornithological interest. Permit required from Bristol Waterworks Co.
Bowldish Quarry, ST 7055. SSSI. Fossiliferous Lower Lias.
Brean Down, ST 2859. NT. Botanical interest. Migration watch-point.
Bridgwater Bay. NNR, 6,076 acres. Coastal reserve with physiographic interest. Shelduck moulting area, occasional avocet. Permit required for Stert Island.
Catcott Heath, ST 4041. LNR, STNC, SSSI, 17 acres. A part of the Somerset moors. Rich flora and fauna. Permit required.
Cheddar Gorge, ST 4654. Great botanical and geological interest with several fine caves.
Cheddar Reservoir, ST 4454. Ornithological interest especially diving ducks. Permit required from Bristol Waterworks Co.
Chew Valley Lake, ST 5760. 1,210 acres. Outstanding ornithological interest. Permit required from Bristol Waterworks Co.
Durleigh Reservoir, ST 2736. 85 acres. Ornithological interest. View from road.
Ebbor Gorge, ST 5348. NNR, NT, 101 acres. Well wooded Carboniferous Limestone gorge. Geological and botanical interest.

Friary Wood, ST 7958. LNR, STNC, 2 acres. Hazel coppice with beech standards. Varied flora and bird life. Permit required.
Goblin Combe, ST 4765. LNR, STNC, 24 acres. Limestone screes and calcareous grassland. Good natural history interest. Permit required.
Gordano Valley, near Clevedon. Peat deposit. Botanical interest.
Holwell Cave, southern part of the Quantocks. SSSI. Geological interest and rare invertebrates.
Kilmersdon, ST 5072. LNR, STNC, 1.79 acres. Woodland. Permit required.
Langford Heathfield, ST 1023. 176 acres. Grass common with scrub and oak-wood. Rich flora and fauna. Public access.
Leigh Woods, ST 5674. NT. Good botanical and entomological locality.
Long Wood, ST 4855. LNR, STNC, 42 acres. Mixed woodland. Large badger sett. Restricted access.
Mendips. Fine hill range of Carboniferous Limestone. Uncommon calcicoles and many caves with Pleistocene fauna.
Priddy Pools, ST 5450. Good entomological locality.
Prior's Park Wood, ST 2217. LNR, STNC. Calcareous woodland. Ornithological interest. Roe deer. Permit required.
Quantocks. Hill range of great scenic beauty. Moorland with wooded combes. Good botanical, entomological and ornithological interest.
Rodney Stoke, ST 4950. NNR. Fine example of Mendip ashwood associated with other trees. Good calcareous flora. Permit required.
Shapwick Heath, ST 4240. NNR, 546 acres. Raised bog with rich flora and fauna. Permit required.
Sharpham Moor, ST 4638. LNR, SPNR, Part of the North Levels. Rich fauna and flora.
Steep Holm, ST 2260. Botanical interest and bird-ringing station. Very restricted access.
Sutton Bingham Reservoir, ST 5410. 145 acres. Ornithological interest.
Swildon's Hole, Priddy. SSSI. Cave of great scenic value and varied invertebrate fauna.
Westhay, ST 4543. LNR, STNC, 30 acres. Raised bog. Permit required.
Wookey Hole, ST 5348. Famous limestone cavern with Pleistocene fauna.

Wiltshire

Bentley Wood, SU 2530. 3,100 acres. Forestry Commission woodland with botanical interest.
Britford, SU 1628. Good area for wild life on the Avon. Several footpaths give access.
Charnage Quarry, Mere, ST 8332. Chalk fossils.
Coate Water, SU 1783. Winter wildfowl.

Corsham Lake, ST 8770. Winter wildfowl. Private estate open Sundays in winter—admission charge.
Cotley Hill, ST 9143. LNR, WTNC. Downland butterflies. Permit required.
Dinton Sand-pit, SU 0131. Fossiliferous Upper Greensand.
Fyfield Down, SU 1471. NNR, 612 acres. Large representative area of high chalk downland with sarsen stones. Permit required apart from footpaths.
Ham Hill, SU 3361. LNR, WTNC, 4½ acres. Interesting flora. No access at present.
Kennet and Avon Canal. Rich in aquatic life. Tow path accessible from many road bridges.
Longford Castle Lake, SU 1726. Private estate. Winter wildfowl, especially teal and diving duck.
Longleat Lakes, ST 8143. Private estate, open daily. Winter wildfowl.
Nadder Island, SU 1130. LNR, WTNC. Small island in the Nadder, near Salisbury. Permit required.
Pepperbox Hill, SU 2124. NT, 73 acres. Downland flora.
Pewsey Down, SU 1063 and 1263. NNR, 188 acres. Botanical and entomological interest. Permit required.
Red Lodge and Somerford Common, SU 0689 and 0286. LNR, WTNC. Old woodland.
Rodbourne Sewage Farm, SU 1585. Wader migration. Permission required.
Savernake Forest, south-east of Marlborough. Ancient woodland of great botanical and entomological interest. Red, fallow and roe deer.
Upper Thames meadows. Fritillary fields.
Whitesheet Hill, ST 8034. LNR, WTNC, NT. Chalk flora.

Nature trails

Permanent nature trails are on the increase although some areas are better endowed than others; in addition, temporary trails are often constructed for special events. The following list, however, is as comprehensive a record of the permanent trails as possible at the time of preparation.

Dorset

Brownsea Island, SZ 0288. Guided tours for public in summer. Charge made. Regular boat service from Sandbanks and Poole Quay. Also tree trail in summer, leaflet 5p.
Durlston Head, SZ 0477. Cliff-top trail during June and July. Leaflet on site.
Puddletown Forest Walk, SY 7492, 2 miles south of Puddletown. 1–3 miles. Coniferous woodland. Leaflet on site.
Studland Heath, SZ 0383. Two trails, shore and woodland. Start at Knoll House Car Park. Leaflet on site.

Thorncombe Wood near Dorchester, SY 7292. April to September. Mixed woodland. Leaflet on site.
Wareham Forest Walk, SY 9089. Start 1 mile north-west of Wareham. 2¼ miles. Coniferous woodland and heath. Leaflet available on site.

Hampshire and the Isle of Wight

Bembridge Trail. Long distance, Shide to Bembridge, approx 15 miles. Chalk downs, woodland, marshland, good views. Guide from County Surveyor, County Hall, Newport, Isle of Wight.
Bere Forest near Wickham, SU 5912. Forest walks 1½ or 2½ miles. Leaflet available.
Blackgang, SZ 4876. 2¼ miles. Coastal cliffs on Cretaceous deposits. Leaflet from Tourist Board, Newport, Isle of Wight.
Bolderwood, New Forest, SU 2407. Arboretum and fallow deer. Guide from Lyndhurst office of Forestry Commission, 4p.
Brighstone Forest, Isle of Wight, SZ 4184. Wood and downland, fine views. Booklet, which includes Parkhurst walk, from Tourist Board, Newport, Isle of Wight or from the Forester, Ridget Lane, Mottistone.
Brook, Isle of Wight, SZ 3983. 2 miles. Start from Seely Hall. Leaflet from Tourist Board, Newport, Isle of Wight.
Butser Hill, SU 7120. HCC, open space—downland trail. Leaflet available.
Danebury Hill, SU 3237. HCC, open space—chalk down and beech woodland. Leaflet available.
Hamstead Trail, Isle of Wight. Long distance, Hamstead Ledge to Brook, approx 7 miles. Guide from County Surveyor, County Hall, Newport, Isle of Wight.
Hengistbury Head, SZ 1890. Varied coastal habitats. 2 miles. Leaflet available.
Isle of Wight Coastal Path. Approx 65 miles and not continuous.
Medina River, Isle of Wight. Approx 3 miles. Salt marsh. Start from Newport Quay. Leaflet from Tourist Board, Newport, Isle of Wight.
Newtown, Isle of Wight, SZ 4191. IOWCC. Salt marsh and woodland, 2 miles. Leaflet from warden, Marsh Farmhouse, Newtown, 7½p.
Nunwell Trail, Isle of Wight. Long distance, Oakfield, Ryde, to Lake Common. Guide from County Surveyor, County Hall, Newport.
Old Winchester Hill, SU 6421. NNR. Two trails, 1 mile and 1¾ miles. Small natural history collection in hut if warden is on site. Leaflet available.
Parkhurst Forest Walk, Isle of Wight, SZ 4792. Up to 2½ miles. Drive through Bulls Gate off Forest Road to car park. Booklet from Tourist Board, Newport or from FC office at Signal House.
Rhinefield Ornamental Drive, SU 2606. FC arboretum. Start 3 miles south-west of Lyndhurst. 1½ miles. Leaflet from FC, Queens House, Lyndhurst.

Rowhill Nature Reserve, Aldershot, SU 8549. Varied habitats. Guide can be bought from Heath End Nurseries, Farnborough Road, Heath End, Farnham, during business hours.
Shepherds Trail, Isle of Wight. Long distance, Whitcombe Cross to Atherfield, approx 10 miles. Guide from County Surveyor, County Hall, Newport.
Stenbury Trail, Isle of Wight. Long distance, Blackwater to Week Down, Ventnor, approx 10 miles. Valley and downland. Start from Birchmore Farm, near Newport. Guide from County Surveyor, County Hall, Newport.
Tennyson Trail, Isle of Wight. Long distance, Carisbrooke to Alum Bay, 15 miles. Varied habitats. Start from Nodgham Lane, Carisbrooke. Guide from County Surveyor, County Hall, Newport.
Worsley Trail, Isle of Wight. Long distance, Brighstone Forest car park to St Blasius Church, Shanklin, approx 15 miles. Guide from County Surveyor, County Hall, Newport.

Somerset

Avon Gorge, ST 5575. FC, mixed woodland. Three walks, ⅔, 1 and 1¼ miles. Leaflet available.
Biddle Combe near Wells, ST 5646. Wooded Mendip combe, 2½ miles. Leaflet from Wells Museum, 2½p.
Castle Neroche near Taunton, ST 2715. FC, mixed woodland. Leaflet available.
Ebbor Gorge, ST 5248. NNR. Start from car park. Leaflet available.
Kennet and Avon Canal, Widcombe to Bathampton, ST 7565. City of Bath nature trail. Start Spring Gardens near Bath railway station. 2 miles. Leaflet from Bath Parks Dept.
Long Wood, ST 4855. STNC. Woodland trail. Booklet from Reserves Officer, Southwell House, Trull, Taunton.
Quantock Forest Trail, ST 1737. Start at Seven Wells Bridge, north side of Quantocks. 3 miles. Leaflet available.
Wells, ST 5545. Quarry and woods 2½–3 miles. Leaflet from Wells Museum, 2½p.

Wiltshire

Brokerswood near Westbury. Eight trails up to 1 mile. Natural history centre and museum. Guide, including admittance to centre, 22p; accompanied children under 14 free.
Marden, between Calne and Chippenham. April to September. Disused railway line with abundant wild life. Guide from Calne and Chippenham RDC, Bewley House, Marshfield Road, Chippenham, 10p.
Savernake Forest, SU 2068. FC, woodland. Start at picnic site where leaflet available.

Naturalists' trusts, societies, field study centres and research laboratories

Berkshire

Berkshire, Buckinghamshire and Oxfordshire Naturalists' Trust, Berks county sec, Mr B. Baker, The Museum, Reading.

Middle Thames Natural History Society, Mr S. C. Finch-Davies, Beech Cottage, 14 Westfield Road, Beaconsfield, Bucks. (Includes Berkshire east of the Loddon.)

Newbury and District Field Club, The Museum, Newbury, Berks.

Newbury District Ornithological Club, Mr R. G. Webb, 69 Boundary Road, Newbury, Berks.

Reading and District Natural History Society, Mrs K. Rhodes, 65 Tilehurst Road, Reading, Berks.

Reading Ornithological Club, Mr B. G. Hamblin, 163 Wykeham Road, Reading, Berks.

Sutton Courtenay Field Study Centre for Schools, 15 acres and hutments in grounds of Didcot Power Station. In conjunction with BBONT.

Dorset

Dorset Naturalists' Trust, Miss H. J. Brotherton, OBE, JP, Island View, 58 Pearce Avenue, Parkstone, Poole, Dorset.

Dorset Natural History and Archaeological Society, Mr R. N. R. Peers, MA, AMA, Secretary and Curator, County Museum, High West Street, Dorchester, Dorset.

Freshwater Biological Association River Laboratory, East Stoke, Wareham.

Furzebrook Research Station, Nature Conservancy, Wareham.

Portland Bird Observatory and Field Centre, Warden Mr F. R. Clafton, The Old Lower Light, Portland Bill, Dorset.

South Dorset Bird Watchers' Society, Mr J. J. Tann, Mandeville, 154 Newstead Road, Weymouth, Dorset.

West Dorset Naturalists' Association, Mr R. Branwhite, 3 Henhayes Lane, Crewkerne, Somerset.

Hampshire and the Isle of Wight

Hampshire and Isle of Wight County Naturalists' Trust, Lt-Col V. W. Tregear, King John's Lodge, Romsey, Hants.

Hampshire Field Club and Archaeological Society, Ornithological Section, Mr P. J. Puckering, 17 Taplings Road, Weeke, Winchester, Hants.

Aldershot Naturalists' Society, Mrs A. Thomas, Willow Croft, Withies Lane, Compton, Guildford.

Alton Natural History Society, Mr N. MacLeod, Farringdon Place, Alton, Hants.

Andover Natural History Society, Miss J. Farmer, 11 Weyhill Road, Andover.

Avon Valley Ecological Society, Mr K. G. Goodyear, FRES, 26 Twynham Avenue, Christchurch, Hants.

Basingstoke Field Society, Dr A. R. Fraser, 2 Scotney Road, Basingstoke, Hants.

Bournemouth Natural Science Society, 39 Christchurch Road, Bournemouth, Hants.

Eley Game Advisory Station and Game Research Association, Fordingbridge, Hants.

Fawley Power Station Marine Laboratory and Aquarium, Central Electricity Generating Board laboratory for marine research, particularly into effect of warm water discharges on marine life.

Isle of Wight Natural History and Archaeological Society, Mr D. W. Axten, Chalk Down, Adgestone Lane, Brading, Sandown, Isle of Wight.

Lymington Natural History Society, Mr S. Keith-Walker, Hawklea, Lower Pennington Lane, Lymington.

Portsmouth and District Natural History Society, Miss F. R. Stranack, 4 Chessington, Craneswater Park, Southsea, Hants.

Ringwood Natural History Society, Mrs E. P. Homfray, Foxhill, Avon Castle Drive, Ringwood.

Southampton Natural History Society, Mr P. Soanes, 12 Lancaster Road, Maybush, Southampton, Hants.

South-west Hampshire branch of British Naturalists' Association, Mr E. Pope, 33 Pine Crescent, Highcliffe, Hants.

Somerset

Somerset Trust for Nature Conservation, Mr P. Tolson, Porters Cottage, Thurloxton, Taunton, Somerset.

Somerset Archaeological and Natural History Society, Mr C. A. Cookson, OBE, MA, Taunton Castle, Somerset.

Somerset Archaeological and Natural History Society, Ornithological Section, Miss E. M. Palmer, Highfield, Sandford Hill, Bridgwater, Somerset.

Bath Geological Society, Miss A. Davison, Hillside House, Timsbury, Bath, Somerset.

Bath Natural History Society, Miss J. Robinson, 59 Warminster Road, Bathampton, Bath, Somerset.

Box Archaeological and Natural History Society, Miss G. Huggins, 24 Warminster Road, Bath, Somerset.
Bristol Naturalists' Society, c/o The City Museum, Queen's Road, Bristol 8.
Bristol Ornithologists' Club, Mr D. E. Ladham, Willow Lodge, Chew Stoke, Bristol.
Burnham-on-Sea Archaeological and Natural History Society, Mr R. Hill, Leigh House, Brent Knoll, Somerset.
Mid-Somerset Naturalists' Society, Mrs J. Littlewood, 21 Webdon Rise, Bridgwater, Somerset.
South Somerset branch of British Naturalists' Association, Mr C. J. Cornell, 88 Chelston Avenue, Yeovil, Somerset.
Wells Natural History and Archaeological Society, Dr F. S. Wallis, The Museum, Wells, Somerset.
Yeovil and District Natural History Society, Mr J. G. Keylock, Sunnyside, East Street, Crewkerne, Somerset.

Wiltshire

Wiltshire Trust for Nature Conservation, Mrs B. Fergusson, Wake House, Ebbesbourne, Wake, Salisbury, Wilts.
Wiltshire Archaeological and Natural History Society, Mrs G. Seccombe-Hett, 9 Coppershell, Gastard, Corsham, Wilts.

Salisbury and District Natural History Society, Mr E. G. Grange, 9 Tollgate Road, Salisbury, Wilts.
Salisbury and South Wiltshire Geological Society, Mrs C. J. Williams, 9 Riverbourne Road, Milford, Salisbury, Wilts.
Swindon Natural History Society, 2 Winterslow Road, Penhill, Swindon, Wilts.

Museums

Berkshire

Abingdon Borough Museum. Local fossil remains. Daily 2–5.
Newbury Museum. Weekdays except Wed 10–12.30, 1.30–5; Wed 10–12.30. Closing time 4pm during winter.
Reading Museum. Weekdays 10–5.30.

Dorset

Bridport Museum. Open mornings during summer. More restricted in winter.

Dorchester Museum. Weekdays 10–1, 2–5. Large fossil collection, marine life section, Dr Day's Dorset insect collection.

Lyme Regis, Philpot Museum. Daily during summer 10–1, 2.30–5.30. More restricted during winter. Good geological collection and selective collection of shells housed in interesting old building of character.

Poole Museum. Weekdays 10–5. Local fauna (specialising in seabirds).

Portland Museum. Wakeham. Daily during summer 10–5. Includes local fossils.

Sherborne Museum at Abbey Gate House. Easter to October weekdays except Mon, 10.30–12.30, 3–4.30. Sun 3–5. More restricted in winter.

Hampshire and the Isle of Wight

Alton, Curtis Museum. Local geology and natural history. Mon, Tues, Thurs and Fri 2–5. Sat 10–1, 2–5.

Basingstoke, Willis Museum. Tues–Sat 10–12.30, 1.30–5.30, Mon afternoon only. Local geology.

Bournemouth Museum, 39 Christchurch Road, Bournemouth. Private museum for members of Bournemouth Natural Science Society. Otherwise open by arrangement with curator.

Bournemouth, Russell-Cotes Geological Terrace, East Cliff. Fine outdoor collection of British rocks—catalogue available from adjacent museum.

Christchurch, Red Museum. Natural history section. Weekdays 11–1, 2.15–5. Sun 2.15–5.

Portsmouth, Cumberland House Museum, Eastern Parade, Southsea. Includes natural history. Daily Nov–Feb 10–4, March, April, Sept and Oct 10–6, May–Aug 10–9.

Sandown Geological Museum, Isle of Wight. Weekdays except Wed, April–Oct 10–1, 2–5.30. More restricted in winter. Large collection of local fossils. Also cores from local oil drilling.

Selborne, The Wakes, April–Oct daily except Fri 11–1, 2.30–5.30. Sun 2.30–5.30. Gilbert White personalia.

Southampton University Geology Department. Small display collection of geological material open to public during term time.

Winchester, Hampshire County Council Museum Service. HQ of county museum material. No access without appointment.

Somerset

Bath Geological Museum. Well set-out modern museum on second floor of Reference Library, Queen Square, Bath.

Glastonbury, The Tribunal, High Street. Daily 10–1, 2.15–5.15. Mainly antiquities but interesting collection of fossil bird bones.

Shepton Mallet. Mon–Fri 9–1, 2–5. Small museum with a few good local fossils.

Taunton Castle. Mon–Fri 9.30–1, 2.15–5.30. Sat 9.30–5.30. Good spacious collections. Great Bustard. Freshwater fish in aquaria.

Wells. Weekdays April–Sept 10–6. Sun during July, Aug and Sept 2.30–5.30. More restricted in winter. Natural history room. Geological room with fine collection of local rocks, minerals and fossils.

Weston-super-Mare. Mon–Fri 10–6. Sat 10–5. Bird room. South gallery has good Pleistocene exhibits with animal remains from local caves.

Yeovil, Wyndham Museum. Weekdays except Thurs 10.30–1, 2.15–5. Mainly local antiquities with a few birds and local mineral specimens.

Wiltshire

Coate, Richard Jefferies Museum. April–Sept Wed, Sat and Sun 2–5. Oct–March Wed and Sat 2–5. Jefferies personalia housed in his birthplace.

Devizes, Museum of Wiltshire Archaeological and Natural History Society. Open to the public Tues–Sat 11–5. Winter closing time 4pm. Good natural history and geological sections.

Salisbury and South Wiltshire Museum, St Ann Street. Weekdays May–Sept 10–5. Winter closing time 4pm. Good show-case of Great Bustard but principally a folk and archaeological museum.

Swindon Museum. Weekdays 10–6, Sun 2–5. Well set out. Birds, mammals, general collection of minerals, local fossils.

Map list

Ordnance Survey 1in maps covering the region are sheet numbers 156, 157, 158, 159, 165, 166, 167, 168, 169, 177, 178, 179, 180, 181.

1in geological maps are now available for almost all the region. These are drift editions except where indicated otherwise.

251	Malmesbury (S & D)	299	Winchester
254	Henley-on-Thames	300	Alresford
255	Beaconsfield	301	Haslemere (S & D)
264	Bristol (S & D)	311	Wellington
265	Bath (S & D)	312	Yeovil (S & D)
266	Marlborough	313	Shaftesbury
267	Hungerford	314	Ringwood
268	Reading	315	Southampton
269	Windsor	316	Fareham
280	Wells (S & D)	326	Sidmouth

281 Frome (S & D)
282 Devizes
283 Andover
284 Basingstoke
285 Aldershot
295 Taunton
296 Glastonbury (S & D)
297 Wincanton (S & D)
298 Salisbury
327 Bridport
327 Bridport (S)
328 Dorchester
329 Bournemouth
330 Lymington
331 Portsmouth (S with D)
341 West Fleet
342 Weymouth
343 Swanage (S & D)

There are two special locality geological sheets:
Isle of Wight Special Sheet (Drift)
Bristol Special Sheet (Solid and Drift)

Check list of birds in the region appearing in the text, arranged in the Wetmore Order

Black-throated diver	*Gavia arctica*
Great northern diver	*Gavia immer*
Red-throated diver	*Gavia stellata*
Great-crested grebe	*Podiceps cristatus*
Red-necked grebe	*Podiceps griseigena*
Slavonian grebe	*Podiceps auritus*
Black-necked grebe	*Podiceps nigricollis*
Little grebe	*Podiceps ruficollis*
Pied-billed grebe	*Podilymbus podiceps podiceps*
Leach's fork-tailed petrel	*Oceanodroma leucorrhoa*
Fulmar petrel	*Fulmaris glacialis*
Cormorant	*Phalacrocorax carbo*
Shag	*Phalacrocorax aristotelis*
Heron	*Ardea cinerea*
Little bittern	*Ixobrychus minutus*
Bittern	*Botaurus stellaris*
Spoonbill	*Platalea leucorodia*
Mallard	*Anas platyrhyncha*
Teal	*Anas crecca*
Garganey	*Anas querquedula*
Gadwall	*Anas strepera*
Wigeon	*Anas penelope*
Pintail	*Anas acuta*
Shoveler	*Spatula clypeata*
Mandarin	*Aix galericulata*

Scaup-duck	*Aythya marila*
Tufted duck	*Aythya fuligula*
Pochard	*Aythya ferina*
Golden-eye	*Bucephala clangula*
Long-tailed duck	*Clangula hyemalis*
Velvet-scoter	*Melanitta fusca*
Common scoter	*Melanitta nigra*
Eider	*Somateria mollissima*
Red-breasted merganser	*Mergus serrator*
Smew	*Mergus albellus*
Shelduck	*Tadorna tadorna*
White-fronted goose	*Anser albifrons*
Brent goose	*Branta bernicla*
Mute swan	*Cygnus olor*
Whooper swan	*Cygnus cygnus*
Bewick's swan	*Cygnus bewickii*
Buzzard	*Buteo buteo*
Sparrow-hawk	*Accipiter nisus*
Honey-buzzard	*Pernis apivorus*
Marsh-harrier	*Circus aeruginosus*
Hen-harrier	*Circus cyaneus*
Montagu's harrier	*Circus pygargus*
Osprey	*Pandion haliaetus*
Hobby	*Falco subbuteo*
Peregrine falcon	*Falco peregrinus*
Gyr-falcon	*Falco rusticolus*
Kestrel	*Falco tinnunculus*
Black grouse	*Lyrurus tetrix*
Red-legged partridge	*Alectoris rufa*
Partridge	*Perdix perdix*
Quail	*Coturnix coturnix*
Pheasant	*Phasianus colchicus*
Water-rail	*Rallus aquaticus*
Spotted crake	*Porzana porzana*
Corn-crake	*Crex crex*
Moorhen	*Gallinula chloropus*
Coot	*Fulica atra*
Great bustard	*Otis tarda*
Oyster-catcher	*Haematopus ostralegus*
Lapwing	*Vanellus vanellus*
Ringed plover	*Charadrius hiaticula*
Little ringed plover	*Charadrius dubius*

Kentish plover	*Charadrius alexandrinus*
Grey plover	*Charadrius squatarola*
Golden plover	*Charadrius apricarius*
Dotterel	*Charadrius morinellus*
Turnstone	*Arenaria interpres*
Snipe	*Capella gallinago*
Jack snipe	*Lymnocryptes minimus*
Woodcock	*Scolopax rusticola*
Curlew	*Numenius arquata*
Whimbrel	*Numenius phaeopus*
Black-tailed godwit	*Limosa limosa*
Bar-tailed godwit	*Limosa lapponica*
Green sandpiper	*Tringa ochropus*
Redshank	*Tringa totanus*
Spotted redshank	*Tringa erythropus*
Knot	*Calidris canutus*
Purple sandpiper	*Calidris maritima*
Little stint	*Calidris minuta*
Pectoral sandpiper	*Calidris melanotos*
Dunlin	*Calidris alpina*
Curlew-sandpiper	*Calidris testacea*
Sanderling	*Crocethia alba*
Avocet	*Recurvirostra avosetta*
Grey phalarope	*Phalaropus fulicarius*
Stone-curlew	*Burhinus oedicnemus*
Skuas	*Stercorarius* spp
Great black-backed gull	*Larus marinus*
Lesser black-backed gull	*Larus fuscus*
Herring gull	*Larus argentatus*
Common gull	*Larus canus*
Mediterranean black-headed gull	*Larus melanocephalus*
Little gull	*Larus minutus*
Black-headed gull	*Larus ridibundus*
Franklin's gull	*Larus pipixcan*
Sabine's gull	*Xema sabini*
Kittiwake	*Rissa tridactyla*
Black tern	*Chlidonias niger*
White-winged black tern	*Chlidonias leucopterus*
Common tern	*Sterna hirundo*
Arctic tern	*Sterna macrura*
Roseate tern	*Sterna dougallii*
Little tern	*Sterna albifrons*

Sandwich tern	*Sterna sandvicensis*
Razorbill	*Alca torda*
Guillemot	*Uria aalge*
Puffin	*Fratercula arctica*
Stock dove	*Columba aenas*
Wood pigeon	*Columba palumbus*
Collared dove	*Streptopelia decaocto*
Cuckoo	*Cuculus canorus*
Barn owl	*Tyto alba*
Little owl	*Athene noctua*
Tawny owl	*Strix aluco*
Long-eared owl	*Asio otus*
Short-eared owl	*Asio flammeus*
Nightjar	*Caprimulgus europaeus*
Swift	*Apus apus*
Kingfisher	*Alcedo atthis*
Green woodpecker	*Picus viridis*
Great spotted woodpecker	*Dendrocopus major*
Lesser spotted woodpecker	*Dendrocopus minor*
Wryneck	*Jynx torquilla*
Wood lark	*Lullula arborea*
Sky lark	*Alauda arvensis*
Swallow	*Hirundo rustica*
House martin	*Delichon urbica*
Sand martin	*Riparia riparia*
Raven	*Corvus corax*
Carrion crow	*Corvus corone*
Rook	*Corvus frugilegus*
Jackdaw	*Corvus monedula*
Magpie	*Pica pica*
Jay	*Garrulus glandarius*
Great tit	*Parus major*
Blue tit	*Parus caeruleus*
Coal tit	*Parus ater*
Marsh tit	*Parus palustris*
Willow tit	*Parus atricapillus*
Long-tailed tit	*Aegithalos caudatus*
Bearded tit	*Panurus biarmicus*
Nuthatch	*Sitta europaea*
Wall creeper	*Tichodroma muraria*
Tree creeper	*Certhia familiaris*
Wren	*Troglodytes troglodytes*

Dipper	*Cinclus cinclus*
Brown thrasher	*Taxostoma rufum rufum*
Mistle thrush	*Turdus viscivorus*
Fieldfare	*Turdus pilaris*
Song thrush	*Turdus philomelos*
Redwing	*Turdus musicus*
Ring ouzel	*Turdus torquatus*
Blackbird	*Turdus merula*
Wheatear	*Oenanthe oenanthe*
Stonechat	*Saxicola torquata*
Whinchat	*Saxicola rubetra*
Redstart	*Phoenicurus phoenicurus*
Black redstart	*Phoenicurus ochrurus*
Nightingale	*Luscinia megarhyncha*
Robin	*Erithacus rubecula*
Cetti's warbler	*Cettia cetti*
Grasshopper warbler	*Locustella naevia*
Reed warbler	*Acrocephalus scirpaceus*
Marsh warbler	*Acrocephalus palustris*
Sedge warbler	*Acrocephalus schoenobaenus*
Blackcap	*Sylvia atricapilla*
Garden warbler	*Sylvia borin*
Whitethroat	*Sylvia communis*
Lesser whitethroat	*Sylvia curruca*
Dartford warbler	*Sylvia undata*
Desert warbler	*Sylvia nana*
Willow warbler	*Phylloscopus trochilus*
Chiffchaff	*Phylloscopus collybita*
Wood warbler	*Phylloscopus sibilatrix*
Pallas's warbler	*Phylloscopus proregulus*
Goldcrest	*Regulus regulus*
Firecrest	*Regulus ignicapillus*
Spotted flycatcher	*Muscicapa striata*
Pied flycatcher	*Muscicapa hypoleuca*
Red-breasted flycatcher	*Muscicapa parva*
Hedge sparrow	*Prunella modularis*
Meadow pipit	*Anthus pratensis*
Tawny pipit	*Anthus campestris*
Olive-backed pipit	*Anthus hodgsoni*
Tree pipit	*Anthus trivialis*
Rock pipit	*Anthus spinoletta petrosus*
Water pipit	*Anthus spinoletta spinoletta*

Pied wagtail	*Motacilla alba yarrellii*
White wagtail	*Motacilla alba alba*
Grey wagtail	*Motacilla cinerea*
Yellow wagtail	*Motacilla flava*
Parula warbler	*Parula americana*
Great grey shrike	*Lanius excubitor*
Woodchat shrike	*Lanius senator*
Red-backed shrike	*Lanius collurio*
Starling	*Sturnus vulgaris*
Hawfinch	*Coccothraustes coccothraustes*
Greenfinch	*Chloris chloris*
Goldfinch	*Carduelis carduelis*
Siskin	*Carduelis spinus*
Linnet	*Carduelis cannabina*
Twite	*Carduelis flavirostris*
Lesser redpoll	*Carduelis flammea cabaret*
Serin	*Serinus canarius*
Bullfinch	*Pyrrhula pyrrhula*
Crossbill	*Loxia curvirostra*
Chaffinch	*Fringilla coelebs*
Brambling	*Fringilla montifringilla*
Yellowhammer	*Emberiza citrinella*
Corn bunting	*Emberiza calandra*
Cirl bunting	*Emberiza cirlus*
Ortolan bunting	*Emberiza hortulana*
Reed bunting	*Emberiza schoeniclus*
Lapland bunting	*Calcarius lapponicus*
Snow bunting	*Plectrophenax nivalis*
House sparrow	*Passer domesticus*
Tree sparrow	*Passer montanus*

Bibliography

Alexander, W. B. *Annotated List of the Birds of Berkshire* (Oxford, 1952)
Alexander, H. G. *A Check-list of the Birds of Purbeck* (Swanage, 1969)
Alvin, K. L. 'Observations on Lichen Ecology of South Haven', *Journal of Ecology*, 48 (1960)
Balfour-Browne, F. 'The Aquatic Coleoptera of South Hampshire', *Ent Gazette*, 3, no 3 (1952)
Ballance, D. K. and Palmer, E. M. *The Birds of Somerset* (1968)
Bath Natural History Society. *Magazine* (Bath)
Beirne, B. P. *British Pyralid and Plume Moths* (1952)
Bournemouth Natural Science Society. *Proceedings* (Bournemouth)
Bowen, H. J. M. *The Flora of Berkshire* (Oxford, 1968)
Bowman, R. P. 'Ecological Survey of Dibden Bottom, New Forest' (unpublished, 1951)
Bristol Naturalists' Society. *Proceedings* (Bristol)
British Association Handbook, *Survey of Southampton and its Region* (Southampton, 1964)
British Association Handbook. *Bristol and its Adjoining Counties* (Bristol, 1955)
Carne, P. H. *History and Distribution of Deer in Dorset* (Dorchester, 1967)
Chatwin, C. P. *British Regional Geology—the Hampshire Basin* (1960)

Clark, R. J. 'Feral Mink in South West England', *Mammal Review*, vol I, no 3 (1970)
Cohen, E. *Birds of Hampshire and the Isle of Wight* (1963)
Coysh, A. W., Mason, E. J. and Waite, V. *The Mendips* (1954)
Cruse, E. J. *Castle Combe* (1965)
Davies, G. M. *The Dorset Coast* (1956)
Denman, D. R., Roberts, R. A. and Smith, H. J. F. *Commons and Village Greens* (1967)
Diver, C. and Good, R. D'O. 'General Scheme of South Haven Survey', *Journal of Animal Ecology*, vol 3, no 2 (1934)
Diver, C. and Diver, P. 'Orthoptera of South Haven', *Journal of Animal Ecology*, vol 2, no 1 (1933)
Donisthorpe, H. 'Coleoptera of the Isle of Wight', *Trans Leicester Lit and Phil Soc*, vol X, pt I (Leicester, 1906)
Dorset Farming and Wildlife Conference. *Farming and Wildlife in Dorset* (1971)
Dorset Natural History and Archaeological Society. *Proceedings* (Dorchester)
Dorset Naturalists' Trust. *Annual Reports* (Dorchester)
Dorset Naturalists' Trust. *The First Ten Years* (Dorchester)
Fitzgerald, B. V. 'Distribution of bats in Hampshire', *Proceedings Hants Field Club*, vol 16 (1944)
Forestry Commission. *New Forest Guide* (1969)
Fraser, F. C. 'Entomological Fauna of the New Forest—Part I, Odonata', *Journal Soc Brit Ent*, vol 3, part 3
Fraser, F. C. 'Entomological Fauna of the New Forest—Part II, Neuroptera', *Journal Soc Brit Ent*, vol 3, part 5
Gardiner, P., Fitter R. and Campbell, B. *Berkshire, Buckinghamshire and Oxfordshire Naturalists' Trust—the first ten years* (1970)
Good, R. D'O. 'Ecology of the flowering plants and ferns of South Haven', *Journal of Ecology*, vol 23 (1935)
Good, R. D'O. *A Geographical Handbook of the Dorset Flora* (Dorchester, 1949)
Grose, D. *The Flora of Wiltshire* (Devizes, 1957)

Hampshire Field Club. *Bird Reports*

Heginbothom, C. D. 'Wiltshire Mollusc Collectors', *Wilts A and N H Mag*, vol 51 (1946)

Hepburn, I. *Flowers of the Coast* (1952)

Hook, O. *Mammal Survey of the New Forest* (unpublished, 1949)

Isle of Wight Natural History and Archaeological Society. *Proceedings*

James, L. and Marshall, C. R. *Isle of Wight Marine Fauna List* (I of W, 1952)

Kite, O. *A Fisherman's Diary* (1969)

Lack, D. 'Breeding bird population of British heaths and moorland', *Journal of Animal Ecology*, vol 4, no 1

Lack, D. and Venables, L. S. V. 'Heathland birds of South Haven Peninsula', *Journal of Animal Ecology*, vol 6 (1937)

Lascelles, G. *Thirty Five Years in the New Forest* (1915)

Lousley, J. E. *Wild Flowers of Chalk and Limestone* (1950)

Macfadyen, W. A. *Geological Highlights of the West Country* (1970)

Mammal Society. *Notes*

Marlborough College Natural History Society. *Annual Reports*

Middle Thames Natural History Society. *Proceedings*

Moore, N. W. 'Heaths of Dorset and their conservation', *Journal of Ecology*, vol 50 (1962)

Newbury and District Field Club. *Proceedings*

Nicholson, E. M. *Britain's Nature Reserves* (1957)

North, F. J. *Evolution of the Bristol Channel* (Nat Mus Wales, 1964)

Peirson, L. G. *Wiltshire Birds* (Devizes, 1959)

Pickford, R. F. *William Smith* (Bath, 1969)

Pickford, R. F. *Charles Moore* (Bath, 1971)

Radford, Dr M. C. *Birds of Berkshire and Oxfordshire* (1966)

Rayner, J. F. *Supplement to Townsend's Flora of Hampshire* (Southampton, 1929)

Read, W. J. 'Plant life in the Hampshire rivers', *Bournemouth Nat Sc Soc*, vol 41

Reading Naturalist. *Proceedings* (Reading)

Royal Agricultural Society of England. *Some Aspects of West Country Farming* (1957)
Salisbury, Sir Edward. *Downs and Dunes* (1952)
Salisbury, Sir Edward. *Weeds and Aliens* (1961)
Society for the Promotion of Nature Reserves. *Farming and Wild Life* (1970)
Somerset Archaeological and Natural History Society. *Proceedings* (Taunton)
Somerset County Council Planning Department. *Peat in Central Somerset—A Planning Study* (Taunton, 1968)
Southampton Natural History Society. 'Annual Reports'; 'Birds of Church Place Inclosure' (unpublished, 1949); 'Survey of Denny Bog' (unpublished, 1950); 'Aquatic Survey at Ipley' (unpublished, 1951)
Stamp, L. Dudley and Hoskins, W. L. *The Common Lands of England and Wales* (1963)
Steers, J. A. (Ed). *Field Studies in the British Isles* (1964)
Steers, J. A. *Coastline of England and Wales* (1964)
Stephens, Marie N. *Otter Report* (1957)
Tatchell, L. *Heritage of Purbeck* (Dorchester, 1954)
Taverner, J. H. *Wildfowl in Hampshire* (Winchester, 1962)
Townsend, F. *Flora of Hampshire* (1883)
Tubbs, C. R. *An Ecological History of the New Forest* (Newton Abbot, 1968)
Tubbs, C. R. 'Numbers of Dartford Warblers in England during 1962–66', *Brit Birds*, vol 60, no 2 (1967)
Varney, W. D. 'Geological History of the Pewsey Vale', *Proc Geol Ass*, vol 32 (1921)
Vaughan, J. *Wild Flowers of Selborne* (1906)
Waite, V. *Portrait of the Quantocks* (1969)
Walton, G. A. 'Fauna of Read's cavern', *Proc Spel Soc Bristol*, vol 5 (1944)
Webber, G. L. *Supplement to Wiltshire Birds—Peirson* (1968)
Webber, N. B. *Investigation of the Seaweed Problem at Cowes Sea Front* (Cowes, 1970)
Whitlock, R. *Salisbury Plain* (1955)

Wightman, R. *Wessex Heathland* (1953)
Williamson, K. 'Habitat preferences of the Wren on English farmland', *Bird Study*, vol 16, no 1 (1969)
Wiltshire Archaeological and Natural History Society. *Proceedings*

Acknowledgements

ALMOST WITHOUT EXCEPTION I have received a ready response from both professional and amateur naturalists to my numerous cries for help.

In my own society, Mrs B. Lucas and Mr C. Drake have supplied information on marine life and alien flora respectively; Mr P. Bowman, another member and friend, has made his encyclopaedic knowledge of Hampshire's wild flowers freely available and characteristically has sacrificed his time to deal with my frequent requests for information. I am grateful also to all the other members whose good fellowship I have enjoyed in numerous excursions in the field and whose enthusiasm for the good things of nature have inspired and sustained my own interest.

My friend, Mr P. H. Carne, editor of the publications of the British Deer Society, has filled in the gaps in my knowledge of deer distribution and in the field has led me on the scent of many a deer.

Mr B. Goater, Rear-Admiral Torlesse and the Reverend David Agassiz have been most helpful in supplying information regarding Hampshire Lepidoptera. Mr B. Baker, the Deputy Director of Reading Museum, has performed a similar service with respect to Berkshire Lepidoptera.

Mr K. H. Grinstead and Miss B. Gillam have answered various queries relating to Wiltshire wild life and the latter in conjunction with the Wiltshire Archaeological and Natural History Society has kindly given me permission to reproduce the map illustrating her studies of badgers in Wiltshire.

Mr F. R. Clafton of Portland Bird Observatory, Mr J. G. Keylock, Mrs O. Hallam, Mr J. H. Crothers and Miss J. Robinson have rendered useful assistance. I acknowledge with pleasure help from Mr and Mrs O. Frazer and Mrs M. Seabroke who have updated and in one or two cases corrected information from written sources relating to the Isle of Wight. I am grateful to several officers of the Nature Conservancy from the regional offices at Roughmoor, Taunton and Brimpton, Reading and the Furzebrook Research Station in Dorset for courteous and detailed replies to my written queries. The secretaries or information officers of the various county naturalists' trusts have supplied information about their reserves.

I am much indebted to several people who have willingly given me permission to reproduce their photographs, maps or drawings: Mrs A. Hughes, in conjunction with the Dorset county naturalists' trust, for the aerial photograph of her farm; Mrs P. Knight for the historic photograph of Niton cliff fall; Somerset County Council Planning Department for the drawings of fen plants; Mr H. L. Edlin, the Publicity Officer of the Forestry Commission for the delightful vignettes by Mr C. F. Tunnicliffe; Collins, publishers, for the maps of Littlesea; Mr J. H. Taverner for the wildfowl maps and Mr P. H. Shelford for the Barton section and fossil drawings.

A word of thanks is due to a public service which I feel is rather taken for granted; I refer to the public libraries. Library staff all over the region have rendered me most helpful service and it is a pleasure to record my gratitude.

My sincere thanks also go to my wife who has assisted me with the map reproductions, the checking, revising and typing.

Finally, in a book which attempts to cover so many natural history interests, errors are always a possibility. Responsibility for any which have occurred in this book is, of course, mine alone.

Index

Italic figures indicate illustrations